BEASTIES

Wee sleekit, cowrin, tim'rous beastie,
O, what a panic is in thy breastie!
Wi' bickering brattle!
I wad be laith to rin an' chase thee,
Wi' murdering prattle!

Robert Burns

by
Louise Binder Scott

Cover Art by Jane Shasky
Inside illustrations by Liza Sernett

Publishers
T. S. Denison & Company, Inc.
Minneapolis, Minnesota 55431

All poems and activities in this book are the author's original contributions unless specified otherwise.

Standard Book Number: 513-02003-9
Printed in the United States of America
Copyright © 1990 by T. S. Denison & Co., Inc.
Minneapolis, MN 55431

CONTENTS

BEASTIES

Beasties is a book of seventy five poems and information about living creatures. There are few children who are not fascinated with pets, birds, insects, animals in the zoo, and other "beasties." If young children are allowed to select books, those of the animal family are invariably the most popular choices. This generalization applies equally to urban and rural children. In schools, classroom pets are often kept. The zoo is visited and sometimes children are allowed to pet certain tame animals. Some zoos or pet stores allow the school to "adopt" an animal for a short period of time.

Children are "naturals" for poetry. All children play, and play is a kind of poetry, for it has rhythm. A love of poetry brings with it a sixth sense that makes children feel alive and gives them mental discipline. When left to themselves to decide, usually they will choose poems that *rhyme* and are fun to do.

The purposes of *Beasties* are:
    to introduce the study of natural science to young children through poetry;
    to improve listening skills, language, and speech development;
    to instill a love of poetry;
    to emphasize child participation through group speaking and conversation
    to develop reasoning; and
    to entertain.

Grade Levels

Grade levels are not designated. Children will enjoy listening to the poems as early as *preschool* and *kindergarten*. They have already experienced group speaking when participating in finger plays, action rhymes, and flannel board stories. *First* and *second* graders love animals and will attend and be able to join in saying refrains. *Third*, and *fourth* graders, and children in remedial classes will want to learn more about the *Beasties* and will be able to engage in a higher level of oral participation and reasoning.

Divisions

Beasties is divided into five sections:
    insects
    birds
    pets
    zoo
    woods, meadows, prairie and stream
This book concludes with a section of pantomimes, quizzes and matching games.

Teaching Poems

The poems in this book are "teaching" poems to be presented by the teacher. *Beasties* offers a collection of rhymes which are easy to learn and which will integrate with any natural science program. Most of the poems are arranged for group or choral speaking. Shorter ones can be written on wall charts and tacked to the bulletin board, then recorded and the recording played back for evaluation. These can be learned easily. Lengthy poems may be divided into sections for group speaking. The teacher may *write* or *type the parts for children who can read*. The entire poem is memorized more easily when each child has a role, although complete memorization is unimportant - unless used for programming.

The children may bring in animal books from the public library to share. They may construct aids such as puppets. They may make scrapbooks of their favorite poems.

The main focuses are upon natural sciences, an appreciation for poetry, and the development of reasoning, speech, and oral communication.

Each lesson with a poem is divided into four parts:
    Introduction of the poem
    Something to do and say for language and reasoning practice
    Activities
    Additional information for learning more about *Beasties*.

The Teacher's Role

The teacher reads the poem to the class, she watches for reactions from the children and notes their ability to listen attentively.

The teacher asks questions. Examples: Have you seen a woodpecker? Where? What was it doing? What kind of sound did it make? What did you learn about the woodpecker after hearing the poem? Would you want one for a pet? Why? *Yes* and *no* responses should not be encouraged.

The teacher finds a picture of a woodpecker in the picture file, encyclopedia or a book about birds. Encourage children to bring animal and bird books from the public library.

The teacher reads the poem again and encourages the children to help say any parts they remember. The poem may be recorded and played back. If the child has a refrain he/she can practice it, then help record when he/she is ready.

The teacher chooses volunteers to say refrains. A group may be selected or one child.

The teacher may write lines or verses on a wall chart if the selection is too long. No pressure to memorize a poem should be made.

The teacher may omit refrains to be said by the children when he or she reads or records the poem. Children take pride in learning their "parts."

The above teachers' roles are only suggestions. Many innovative teachers can devise their own plans for using a poem.

Beasties is not a children's trade book, but rather one which the teacher uses for suggested lesson plans. Emphasize that saying poems together is fun. Experiment with poems children already know and have memorized, such as action rhymes they have learned in kindergarten. Practice prose. *The Pledge of Allegiance* which is a form of group speaking. Copy words on the board occasionally and ask which ones, *skip, hop, run, whisper, sing*; are said *slowly, sadly, happily* or *quickly*. Say a word and ask which emotion it creates (How does it make you feel?).

Use a tape recorder. Children say designated (verses), record them, and evaluate their performace.

Bring in books from the library for the browsing table and use an encyclopedia for the children's own research.

Copy with a marker only lines a child may have trouble recalling, not the entire poem.

Make A Wall Chart For Evaluation

I tried to say words slowly.
I tried to stay with the group.
I tried to pronounce words plainly.
I tried to keep from sounding "sing-song."
I tried to "paint pictures:" with my voice.
I tried to use expressions on my face to make the words more meaningful.
I tried to understand the meaning of all the words.

Group Speaking

Beasties emphasizes oral language as well as the study of animals. The children improve their use of language and speech through a device called group or choral speaking which is the art of saying poetry or prose, using a variety of arrangements. These may include a verse (one line), a couplet (two lines) or a stanza (more than two lines).

Solos: The teacher asks volunteers to say certain lines (verses as he or she reads the rest of the poem.) A number of children may take turns saying lines.

Line-a-child: Children say one line each until the poem ends. Their lines may be indicated by numerals. This practice allows every child to have a turn. An entire poem can be learned in this way. Pressure to learn a poem should never be exerted.

Group: A group or all of the children say only a refrain or stanza which may occur several times.

Boys and Girls: Divide the group so that all children have a chance to participate. Girls say a stanza, then boys, and so on. This arrangement can also take place by rows.

Questions and Answer: A group or one child reads the question, another answers.

All: The children say all of the poem simultaneously with the teacher, saying as many lines or verses as they can recall. This arrangement is appropriate if the children are to *learn* a poem for a parent-teacher program.

Values of Group Speaking

Children who fear speaking will find oral expression easier when participating with a group. These children build *self confidence* and *ego strength* without feeling that others are listening to their possible mistakes. Fear of hearing one's own voice disappears and the self-conscious child becomes more socially confident. Many inhibitions can be overcome when the child is not speaking alone.

All children participate either individually or with a group.

Interest in poetry is built. Poems contain information which children will recall.

Children gain mentally as they are able to use language more effectively.

INSECT AND ARACHNID BEASTIES

WHAT IS IT?

It flies around with its fluttering wings.
It can't make the sound that a robin sings.
It can't make the sound of a chickadee.
It can't make the sound of the rushing sea.
It can't make the sound of the cawing crow.
It can't make the sound of the falling snow.
It can't make the sound of the whispering breeze.
It can't make the sound of the bumblebees.
Fluttering quieter than a sigh
Have you guessed? It's a butterfly!

Something to do and say: There is a line for each of eight children. After reading the poem, ask the children how they would say a specific line (verse): *quietly, slowly, quickly, loudly*; and tell why. Ask: "How did the poem make you feel? Why did you like it?" You may want to write your own poem about a butterfly.

THE BUTTERFLY

They sky was dark, the wind was cold,
And leaves began to fly.
A caterpillar striped with green said,
"I must say good-by."

I'll find a leaf and hang head down.
My skin is getting old,
So I'll exchange it for a skin
Of green with tips of gold."

The north wind sang a lullaby,
As snug and safe she lay.
Then April came, and by and by
Her dry skin dropped away.

So now as pretty insect sat,
And spread her wings to fly.
She sailed the sky on golden wings-
A Monarch butterfly!

Something to do and say: Divide the poem into stanzas. Two for boys and two for girls. Ask the class what they learned about butterflies. Have they seen one? Where? Why do they like this insect? Bring in books from the library that picture butterflies. Suggest that the children draw and color them.

Learning More About Butterflies

A butterfly is the most beautiful insect in the world. It carries pollen to flowers and as a result we have fruit. Caterpillars hatch from its eggs and then turn into butterflies. Butterflies do no harm. They are found everywhere in the world. They fly during the day, while moths fly at night. When resting, butterflies fold their wings over their heads. They have feelers. There are many kinds of butterflies. Encyclopedias label them and show their colorful pictures.

Making a Butterfly Puppet

A butterfly puppet is easily made. Fold a small strip of construction paper in the middle in a ring so it will fit the finger - one to fit your finger for demonstration and one to fit a child's index finger. Glue the ends. Glue a small butterfly shape on the front. The children may trace or draw butterfly shapes and attach strings to the heads. These can then become a mobile or the children can hold the strings and pretend their butterfly is flying.

THE SHY LITTLE CATERPILLAR

A shy little caterpillar looked at the sky.
He hugged a leaf stem and he gave a big sigh.
The sky and the stem didn't make a reply,
He did not understand and he didn't know why.
He hid from the bluejays so quick and so sly.
He hid from the chipmunk so swift and so spry;
He hid from the ant family living close by.
"Please, tell us, caterpillar, why are you shy?
Please, little caterpillar, try not to cry."
"I'll try," said the caterpillar, "but I am shy,
I would not be shy if I could just fly.
I know what I'm going to do by and by:
I will spin a fine bed and I'll then say goodby."
A little wind sang him a sweet lullaby.
And when he woke up, his wet wings were dry.
The shy little caterpillar whispered, "Goodby."
He flew to the sky and was no longer shy
Because he had changed to a blue butterfly!

Something to do and say: Have you seen a caterpillar? Where? Tell what you know about a caterpillar. It will be fun to make a list on the chalkboard of every word that rhymes. They all rhyme with *shy* and *fly*. Count the words. How many are there? Tell how a caterpillar becomes a butterfly. Stay still when you go to the meadow. Hold out your hand. A butterfly may come and sit on the palm of your hand. Paint some butterflies for our bulletin board. Butterflies are of all colors. Say some words that describe caterpillars; butterflies. I will write them on the chalkboard.

Making a Caterpillar

Use an egg carton with 4 to 6 bumps. Paint and decorate them with scraps of paper and sequins. Add pipe cleaner antennae.

THE DRAGONFLY

One day, I saw a dragonfly
Beside a walnut tree.
It's body was all red and green,
That's how it looked to me.

Children: That's how it looked to me.

A dragonfly is really shy.
I wonder why they call
That little fly a "dragon"
When it isn't fierce at all.

Children: It isn't fierce at all.

It eats bugs and mosquitoes
That grow and multiply
It will not bite, and so you need
Not fear the dragonfly.

Children: Don't fear the dragonfly.

The dragonfly is made to fly,
And that is why I claim
It should be called an "airplane" fly.
I think I'll change its name.

Children: I think I'll change its name.

Something to do and say: After you have read the poem, ask the children to tell what they learned about the dragonfly. Record the poem for them, omitting the refrain. Read it again and ask them to say the refrain with you. Then record the poem for listening and evaluation. Ask the children to say as much of the poem as they can with you. Show a picture of a dragonfly.

DRAGONFLIES

Children:	Dragonflies, dragonflies, periwinkle blue, Fiery red ones, and green ones , too.
All:	All darting to and fro With wings like thin glass, Sweeping up mosquitos That are crawling in the grass.
Children:	Dragonflies, Dragonflies, periwinkle blue, Fiery red ones, and green ones, too.
All:	Fluttering here and there, I like to look at them Resting as they sit upon A pussywillow stem.
Children:	Dragonflies, dragonflies, periwinkle blue, Firey red ones, and green ones, too.

Something to do and say: Show colored pictures in an encyclopedia. Show different shades of blue and explain *periwinkle*. Present added information to the class.

Learning More About Dragonflies

A dragonfly is beautiful. It is a water insect. The wings are very thin. The wings are like thin glass and they gleam in the sunlight. A dragonfly can be green, brown or blue. Its eyes are very large and it can see things far away. It has six legs covered with spines. It perches on a stem but cannot walk. Its legs look like a little basket when it flies. The dragonfly eats while it is flying. A female may drop her eggs in the water when she lays them. This insect eats harmful insects that destroy crops.

Making a Dragonfly Puppet

Making a dragonfly puppet is easy. Use a cardboard tube for the body. Paint some red and green stripes around it. Glue a small styrofoam ball to the end for a head. Paint the ball a variety of colors. Cut a small styrofoam ball in half to make the eyes and add plain black buttons to the center. Glue on the eyes. Add six curved pipe cleaners for legs. Cut lace or thin plastic for wings with straws underneath to keep them steady. Add two pipe cleaners to the head for feelers. Glue two strips of string or heavy thread to back and use the dragonfly for a mobile.

TINY, SHINY CRICKET

There's a tiny, shiny cricket
That I always like to see.
There's a happy, scrappy cricket,
And he tries to hide from me.

Children: Crr-ick, crr-ick, crrree!
              My cricket hides from me!
On his back are two hard covers,
That protect his gauzy wings.
He can rub those shiny covers,
To make music that he sings.

Children: Crr-ick, crr-ick, crrree!
              My cricket sings to me!
One wing cover has a scraper,
And the other has a file.
And my cricket serenades me,
In his chirpy cricket style.

Children: Crr-ick, crr-ick, crrree!
              My cricket sings to me!
Then after I have gone to bed,
And stars are shining bright,
My happy, scrappy cricket,
Comes to visit me each night.

Children: Crrr-ick, crrr-ick, crrree!
              My cricket visits me!
As he plays his snappy music,
I creep out of bed, and there,
Is that happy, scrappy cricket,
Hiding underneath my chair.

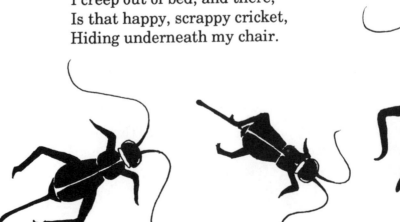

Children: Crr-ick, crrr-ick, crrree!
                My cricket hides from me!
          My room is still at night time.
          Gone to rest is everything,
          But the happy, scrappy cricket
          Thinks it's time to dance and sing.

Children: Crr-ick, crrr-ick, crrree!
                My cricket sings to me!

(Louise Binder Scott and J. J. Thompson, *Talking Time*, McGraw-Hill Book Co., ©1979. Copyright owned by authors)

Something to do and say: When saying the refrain, children may rub palms of hands together or use sand blocks lightly for effect of chirping. A few children may click the tongue, play a guitar string or make the effect using a high voice. Ask which words or lines would be said *softly, quickly, noisily, quietly*. Ask if they have heard or seen a cricket and describe the experience. Record the poem and play it back. Ask the children to tell how they liked it; how it could be improved. Present added information to the class.

Learning More About Crickets

Crickets have feelers at the tips of their abdomens (stomachs). Their wings lie flat over each other on top of their backs. The right wing almost covers the left wing. Each wing has a "file" or a big, thick vein and a "scraper" or hard, sharp-edged part. As the file rubs against the scraper, a sound is made. A cricket lays its eggs on the bark of trees.

Only the male cricket makes sound. All crickets have hearing parts attached to their hind legs. Crickets go out at night for food. They can eat many kinds of foods. Most crickets lay their eggs in the Fall, and in the Spring the eggs hatch.

GRASSHOPPER, GRASSHOPPER

Grasshoppers are clowns. They are skilled acrobats.
Their fiddling makes a strange sound
As they rub together their legs and their wings,
And spend their time buzzing around.

Children: Grasshopper, grasshopper, hopping away,
Grasshopper, grasshopper, singing all day.

Do you know the fable: "Grasshopper and Ant"?
The grasshopper did nothing but shirk.
He never would toil for his food like the ant.
And the poor ant did all of the work.

Children: Grasshopper, grasshopper, hopping away,
Grasshopper, grasshopper, singing all day.

A grasshopper has feelers on top of his head,
And the feelers can help him to smell.
He has two pairs of wings and powerful legs,
And they serve the grasshopper quite well.

Children: Grasshopper, grasshopper, hopping away,
Grasshopper, grasshopper, singing all day.

This little insect is really quite strong.
For hopping, he takes a grand prize.
He could win an olympic championship
For he hops many times his own size.

Children: Grasshopper, grasshopper, hopping away,
Grasshopper, grasshopper, singing all day.

Something to do and say: Ask the children to tell what they remember about the poem. How many hops did the grasshopper make. Choose a few children to hop lightly on the refrain. Ask how the grasshopper makes its sound. How would feelers on top of his head help him? Record the poem and ask the children to evaluate the performance. Present added information as you would a story. Show pictures of a grasshopper.

16

Learning More About Grasshoppers

A mother grasshopper has little hooks at the end of her abdomen (stomach part), and with the hooks she digs a hole in the ground. In the hole she lays up to 100 eggs. There is a sticky foam around the eggs that hardens to protect them through the winter. The baby grasshopper hatches and looks as if it is wrapped in plastic. The baby sheds this covering and its body is covered with a shell. It still has no wings until the shell splits open and it is full grown. Grasshoppers live in all parts of the world except the North and South Poles. Grasshoppers attract mates by making a rattling sound with their wings. Read the fable *The Ant and The Grasshopper* to the children. Dramatize the story.

TWIGS

Twigs is a daddy longlegs
His eight legs are bent and thin.
One day, I tried to count them all
But I could not begin.
The little feelers on his legs -
They're wonderful - so keen
To help him hear and smell and taste;
He keeps them extra clean.
He dines on flies and spiders;
On plants he likes to chew.
When Twigs is really hungry,
'Most anything will do.
      Sometimes his mate lays fifty eggs
      To hatch more daddy long-longlegs!

Something to say and do: Suggest that children learn the poem and record it using one voice. Ask what they learned about a daddy-long-legs. Explain *arachnid*. Tell them that spiders also have eight legs. Present added information to the class as you would a story. Ask children to tell what the remember.

Learning More About Daddy Longlegs
    They are members of the spider family and are called arachnids. The legs are thin and let the insect move very quickly and to keep their bodies high in the air as they run. Ants might harm them otherwise. The eggs are hatched in the earth in spring as the sun warms them up.

THE BUG IN A RUG

A funny, little striped bug,
Lived down inside our fluffy rug.
Upon the floor within our den,
She had a family of ten.
It was a great place for a bug,
Because the rug was soft and snug.
Then one sad day, the cleaner came,
And dear me! Nothing was the same.
It seemed that it was apropos
For bug and family to go.
      But where have they went, I do not know.
      It could have been Ontario
          or Mexico
             or Tokyo!

Something to do and say: Have the children draw a picture of any bug they choose. They ask their friends to guess the name. Think of another place the bugs might go and add to the poem. Tell the children that *apropos* means "appropriate" or the right thing for a bug family to do.

19

THE CENTIPEDE

The centipede, the centipede,
Can run about at greatest speed.
Because it has so many feet
That never even seem to meet.
I wonder if it thinks of shoes
Or if it might wear them by twos!
How could it ever sort them out,
Or know which legs were all about?
When I am walking down the street,
I'd rather have two legs and feet
That do the things I want because
I'd know exactly where I was!

Something to do and say: Find a picture of a centipede. Suggest that children draw one. Ask if they have seen one? Then ask them tell about it. Present added information to the class.

Learning More About The Centipede

The centipede may have from 15 to 170 pairs of legs. It has antennae on its head and two pairs of jaws. The first pair of legs behind its head have claws for fighting, not walking. The claws have poison to protect it. Its body is divided into sections and beneath each section is a pair of legs. Centipedes resemble worms or caterpillars. They eat worms and insects.

MOSQUITO

Mosquito, your song
Will not last very long
If you buzz around here,
A fat frog may appear.

Children: Don't stay around her
A fat frog may appear!

I know you are fond
Of a brook or a pond.
That's where frogs like to play;
Won't you please fly away?

Children: It is dangerous to stay,
Would you please go away?

A frog hops in the garden.
She will not beg your pardon.
But will swallow you down,
And she won't make a frown!

Children: A frog may appear
Go a long way from here!

Mosquito, look out!
A big frog is about
To put out her long tongue,
And your song won't be sung!

Children: Fly away!
Hurry! Zzzzzzzzzzz!

Something to do and say: Say: "Pretend you are a frog, but you cannot fly so the mosquito gets away." Record the poem and play back the recording for evaluation. Which words in the poem are important? Let's make them important with our voices. Tell about an experience with a mosquito. Record the child's story. Present added information to the class.

Learning More About Mosquitoes

Female mosquitoes sting. There are about 2000 kinds of mosquitoes. A mosquito has a round head attached to its chest by a thick neck. It has feelers in front of two round eyes. There are two wings which have scales that can rub off. When a mosquito flies, it moves its wings about 300 times a second. Its legs are long. Mosquitoes hatch eggs. The humming sound is made by wings beating against the body.

THE HORNET

The hornet's dressed in black and yellow
He really is a fancy fellow.
But clothes do not mean anything
Because he has a vicious sting.
I've always found that it is best
Not to go near a hornet's nest!
Zzzzz! OUCH!

Something to do and say: Let's find a picture of a hornet. Have you ever seen one? Tell about it. Do you know of anyone who has been stung? Tell about it. What does the word *vicious* mean?

Learning More About The Hornet

It belongs to the wasp family. There are 2000 kinds of wasps and all have a vicious sting. Hornets build a nest from paper and mud in shrubs or trees close to the ground. They live in communities. When they rest, they fold their wings. They feed on caterpillars and winged insects. Hornets are green or blue in color.

THE LADYBUG PARADE

Tick-tack, tick-tack, see them go -
Dainty little ladybugs marching in a row!
Red ones and yellow ones,
Spotted ones and black,
Plain ones and fancy ones, with round and shiny backs.

Children: Tick-tack, tick-tack, see them go -
              Dainty little ladybugs marching in a row!

With tiny heads and short legs,
And gauzy wings to fly.
Their shiny little wing covers
Keep them safe and dry.

Children: Tick-tack, tick-tack, see them go -
              Dainty little ladybugs marching in a row!

Tick-tack, tick-tack,
Now everybody knows
That aphids in the orange groves
Will gobble all that grows.

Children: Tick-tack, tick-tack,
              The ladybugs have come!
              What happened to the aphids?
              They were eaten, every one!

Something to do and say: As they say the refrain, children may tap on the desk lightly with their fingernails to imitate marching. They can march around the room pretending to be ladybugs. Ask what they learned about ladybugs. Present added information to the class. Paint pictures of ladybugs.

Learning More About Ladybugs

A lady bug is a beetle with a round body. It can be red and yellow with black spots, or just a plain color. Ladybugs eat plant lice, insects, and aphids. (Explain *aphid* - a louse that eats plants.) In California, when aphids almost destroyed the orange crops, barrels of ladybugs were brought in and turned loose to save the crops.

Ladybugs look like tiny-painted cars. There are 4000 kinds of ladybugs. They have two pairs of wings. In England a ladybug is called a "ladybird."

Make Ladybugs

Duplicate a ladybug pattern and invite the children to color their ladybugs. Cut squares of orange construction paper 4" x 4" or 6" x 6". The children tear or cut off corners to make an oval, then cut small circles of black construction paper. Paste the circles on the "bug" and black strips for antennae. Draw features with black crayon. To make a stuffed ladybug, cut two pieces of paper and staple them. Stuff them with crumpled tissue.

MAGICAL BEES

When we were out playing among the fruit trees,
We saw a large beehive and hundreds of bees.
"Oh, bees, won't you tell why you're flying about?"
I said to the bees so that I could find out.
"We fly for sweet pollen to take to the hive.
Oh, it is so wonderful to be alive!
The queen is our mother we all try to please.
She lays many eggs to hatch thousands of bees."
At the door of the hive, soldiers keep a sharp eye,
And only the bees that live here can get by.
The workers are dressed in plain jackets of brown,
And they make many journeys to sweet clover town.
They have bags for the honey you eat on your bread;
And baskets for pollen which they like to spread;
And fuzzy hind legs for their brushes and combs;
And some pockets for wax to make strong beehive homes.
Then there is one bee and its well known
For doing no work because it is a drone.
We said, "Thank you, bees, for telling us why,
You are happy all day as you work and you fly."
We said, "Now we know why you're flying about,
We thank you for helping us learn and find out."
We said to the bees, "There is magic in you,
To do all the wonderful things that you do."

Something to do and say: How much do you remember? What do bees take to the hive? How many eggs will the queen bee hatch? What do the soldiers do? The workers? What does the drone do? Do you like the poem? Why? What do bees make that we spread on bread? Read the poem several times. Ask children to repeat certain lines with you.

Learning More About Bees

Bees are the only insects that produce food eaten by man - honey. We use the beeswax for candles and lipsticks. Many fruits and vegetables would die if bees did not help fertilize them. Bees gather nectar and pollen from flowers. They make honey from the nectar and their food is pollen and honey. They will not sting unless hurt or frightened. They have 6 legs and 4 wings. Bees live together for many years. The queen lays eggs. The workers gather food and take care of young bees. The *drones* mate with the queen. The *queen* does nothing but lay eggs that hatch workers who feed and care for her. The *workers* are females. They carry pollen on their hind legs. Play *"The Flight of the Bumblebee"* by Rimsky-Korsakov.

Make A Bee Puppet

Make a bee stick puppet from black construction paper with glued on yellow strips. Add a dowel stick. Use pipe cleaners for antennae and legs. One group may ask questions and a second group supply answers. Ask: "What did you learn about the bees?"

A DOODLEBUG

A doodlebug digs a deep dugout
And traps all the ants he can eat.
He has ugly jaws, he's round, and he's plump,
With three pairs of legs and six feet.
He walks backward to make his deep dugout.
It's a pit where he traps his small prey.
At the bottom he slugs a poor struggling ant,
Has his dinner and goes on his way.
    He doodles away
    Just eating all day!

Something to do and say: How much do you remember about the doodlebug? Find a picture of a doodlebug to share with us. Perhaps you can draw one.

Learning More About Doodlebugs

The doodlebug is the name of an insect more commonly called the ant lion. It resembles a dragonfly. Doodlebugs dig holes in the ground to trap their food. They like to eat ants and other insects.

THE MAGIC SPARKLER

The firefly has little rings
That circle all around
Its body where a large supply
Of chemical is found.

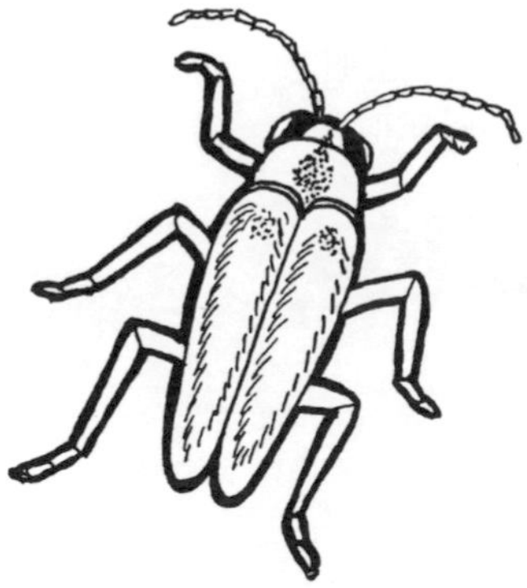

Children: Firefly, firefly,
    Tell me why, firefly.

I try so hard to understand,
And thought I ask it why
It makes a glowing light so bright,
It gives me no reply.

Children: Firefly, firefly,
    Tell me why, firefly.

What light it makes will not burn up,
It will just go and go.
With every little changing spark,
A brighter one will glow.

Children: Firefly, firefly,
    Tell me why, firefly.

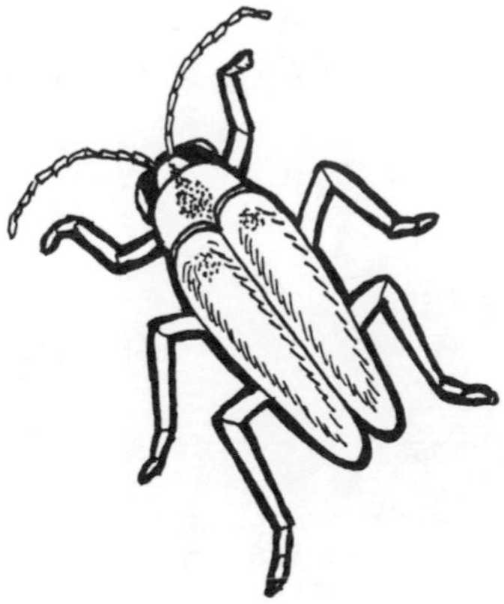

Six-legged insects are such fun
To watch and read about.
Perhaps someday I'll be the one
To find their secrets out.

Children: Firefly, please give me light
    When I am traveling in the night.

Something to say and do: Children say the refrain. One child may hold a flashlight and make the light flicker as the poem is said. Record the poem and encourage children to say as much with you as they can remember.

WHY, FIREFLY?

All: "Oh, Grandpa, what's a firefly
That twinkles in the park?"
I asked, "Why does the glowworm shine
So brightly in the dark?"

Girls: "A glowworm is a firefly,"
My grandpa said to me,
"On glowworms there aren't any wings
Like fireflies, you see."

Boys: "Some people call them lightning bugs.
What is your favorite name?
A lightening bug or firefly?
We know they are the same."

Girls: "But Grandpa, you did not explain
What makes them give a light;
And do they ever catch on fire
Or get too warm at night?"

Boys: My grandpa said, "A firefly
Has rings that circle 'round.
Inside of it, amazingly,
A chemical is found."

Girls: Just how that chemical can burn
Has puzzled wisest men,
Because you see, it won't burn up.
It comes right back again!

Boys: Burn, spark and change,
Burn, spark and change,
As fast as that and quicker!
"Say, Grandpa, now I understand
What makes the firefly flicker."

All: "Yes, that is true," my grandpa said,
"We'd like to know as well,
How we could make cold light like theirs.
A firefly won't tell!"

Something to say and do: After you have read the poem, choose children to participate, and say the lines with them so there will be no embarrassment at forgetting. Memorizing should not be forced. Record the poem yourself and play the recording as the children arrive from recess. Present added information to the class. Ask how much about fireflies has been remembered.

BIRD BEASTIES

All birds have feathers and they live in every part of the world. All birds except an ostrich, a penguin and an emu can fly. All birds hatch from eggs, have two legs and beaks. Their bones are hollow to make them lighter so they can fly. Chickens are poultry, but they are birds that give us eggs and meat. Birds eat insects that might ruin crops of vegetables and grain. They may live on land or water or both. Ducks like water. So do sea gulls. Parrots are tropical birds from South America, Australia or Africa. *Hunters* are eagles, hawks and owls. Kingfishers eat fish. Vultures eat dead animals.

Birds that have their nests in trees or above the ground are *songbirds*: robins, larks, wrens, starlings or thrushes.

Birds eat a lot compared with people. They like seeds and fruit, insects and worms. Owls and hawks eat mice, rats and lizards. Parakeets and parrots can be trained to talk.

Encyclopedias offer colored pictures of most species of birds.

What do you know about birds? Tell us. Which is your favorite bird? Imitate a bird's song. Ask children to find books about birds in the public library. Share them with the class. Go on a "bird watch" to see how many birds you can identify.

THE SCREECH OWL

The screech owl is solemn with circular eyes
Which he never can move, however he tries.
He stares straight ahead when he wishes to see,
And he turns his whole head when he gazes at me.
He sees things by day, but much better at night.
And he usually snoozes through all the daylight.
He makes hardly a whisper when flying around,
And his shrill screech owl cry makes a quivering sound.
When old Mister Screech Owl comes out of his house
To hunt for his dinner, watch out little mouse!

Something to do and say: Children tell what facts they learned about the screech owl. Borrow books about owls from the library. Differentiate types of owls. Perhaps you can borrow a record of bird calls. Present added information to the children as a story. Ask children to tell what they now know about the screech owl.

Learning More About The Screech Owl

A screech owl has keen ears. They hide behind its soft feathers. The owl sleeps during the day. It hunts at night. It has sharp talons on its strong legs. It catches mice. When a screech owl hears a gurgling in the brook, it knows there are snails and crayfish around. If it thinks there is an enemy around, it will pull in its feathers and stretch out long. Its eyes become narrow. In this way, the owl looks like a branch of a tree. By the time a screech owl is three weeks old it can swallow a whole mouse. A grown-up owl can eat its own weight every day. Owls cannot move their eyes.

HELICOPTER BIRD

All:
I saw something sparkle one day in the garden;
A hummingbird almost as small as a bee.
And there as I watched, his green feathers kept changing
Like jewels that flashed many colors to me.

Group 1:
The patch at his throat was as red as a fire,
And then he flew backward (I knew that he would).
Swooping down, up and sideways, that tiny stunt flier
Did things that no pilot or other bird could.

Group 2:
Like a small helicopter, all buzzing and whirring,
He just missed my head as he flew on his way.
His wings beat so fast I saw only a blurring;
A hummingbird was in our garden today.

Group 3:
Hummingbirds like bright colors of red, orange and yellow.
I mixed sugar water I hoped he would try.
It was in a glass jar I wrapped in red paper,
And hung on a limb where I knew he would fly.

Group 4:
He liked it and sipped it for maybe a minute.
And if I kept quiet, he wasn't afraid.
He will chase other birds as his mate gathers cobwebs.
She needs them to finish the nest she has made.

Group 5:
The nest, it is almost as small as a nutshell.
She pounds and she pokes with her bill and her legs.
It is plastered with bark from the place it is fastened.
And there she has hidden her two tiny eggs!

All:
I saw something sparkle one day in the garden
A hummingbird almost as small as a bee;
And there as I watched, his green feathers kept changing
Like jewels that flashed many colors to me.

Something to do and say: Ask what the class learned about hummingbirds. Ask if they have seen one and tell about it. Write a statement from each child and make the statements into a booklet. Ask how a hummingbird could be fed. Why is it called a "helicopter" bird? Record the poem for evaluation. Say the lines along with designated children. Present added information to the class.

Learning More About Hummingbirds

A hummingbird is the smallest bird in the world. About 19 kinds live in the United States. Their wings make a humming sound. The wings move over 60 times a second. Hummingbirds have bright colored feathers that are green, red, violet and orange. They can fly backward, forward, down or up. They have long bills that sip nectar from flowers. The tongue is like a long tube. The mother bird lays two tiny white eggs, each about the size of a bean. The father watches over the nest high up in a tree. In three weeks the babies can leave their nests. Hummingbirds cannot walk.

MR. WOODPECKER

Mr. Woodpecker
  With bright, red hood,
Why do you think
  That bugs are good?
You look and you peck
  Until it is dark.
You peck for goodies
  In old tree bark.
You peck on wood
  And I have found
That you peck on tin
  With a noisy sound.
You peck at at a looking glass
  On a hook.
Once you pecked at the cover
  On my book.

Something to do or say: Children use pencils to drum on a book. Ask for rhyming words: which word rhymes with *hood, look, found* etc. Perhaps they can make up a poem. Present added information to the class.

THE WOODPECKER

The woodpecker has a remarkable bill.
Which serves as a hammer and also a drill.
To drum on a tin roof, he's pleased and content.
It is really a wonder his bill is not bent.

Children: The most amazing bird ever
                Is a woodpecker so clever.

Have you seen how he climbs, how he jumps with both feet,
How his tail makes a prop when he hunts things to eat?
He pecks at the soft-growing bark of a tree,
And he knows where the fat little bugs ought to be.

Children: The most amazing bird ever
                Is a woodpecker so clever.

Mister Woodpecker spears one and eats it, or maybe
He carries it home to his woodpecker baby.
He may wake you up early, but pardon him please.
He's just eating the bugs that are killing your trees!

Children: The most amazing bird ever
                Is a woodpecker so clever.

Something to do and say: Ask children to tell how a woodpecker helps us. Do they like this bird? Why? Ask them to tell about their experiences and write them down. Show a picture of a woodpecker. Present added information to the class and discuss it.

Learning More About Woodpeckers

It has a very strong bill that bores holes in trees. It bores holes to find insects. Woodpeckers have strange toes or claws that can climb up and down trees. Two toes are pointed to the front. Two toes are pointed to the back. Woodpeckers have stiff tail feathers. They have long tongues with little barbs or hooks on the tips. They can spear insects with their tongues. Their voices are loud. Their feathers are spotted black and white or brown and white. Some males have red or yellow feathers on their heads. Most encyclopedias or books on birds have pictures of woodpeckers.

THE ROBIN

Girls: The robin is a cheerful bird.
His happy song is often heard.
"Cheerily," you'll hear him sing.
"Warm Spring days are here to stay."

Boys: Mr. Robin wins "the race"
To get the finest nesting place.
One day in April you may see
Mr. Robin in a tree.

Girls: With soft grasses in his beak.
He builds a nest within a week.
In that nest away up high
Four baby robins soon you'll spy.

Boys: Robin flies at break of dawn
To investigate our lawn.
Marching like a giant tall,
Listens to hear something crawl.

Girls: He finds a juicy earthworm round,
Tugs and pulls it from the ground.
Hungry baby robins squawk,
"We want worms," in robin talk.

Boys: All the worms those babies eat
Would make one worm of fourteen feet.
Babies screech and push. The winner,
Gets the most worms for its dinner!

39

WHY I LIKE ROBINS

Everbody I know likes the robin.
I am sure that you've all had a look
At the grass where a robin is hopping,
Or at one in your own picture book.

One thing that I like about robins
Is the nest that they build in a tree.
Six feet from the ground on low branches.
So if I want to watch, I can see.

Nest building is very important.
Robins make many trips just to get
Soft grasses and mud and hard stubble.
Robins work very hard you can bet!

If a rain or hail storm washes mud out,
The mother repairs it right now.
And fathers tell all other robins,
"Keep away from OUR tree and THIS bough!"

A thing that I like about robins
Is their eggs, three or four, greenish-blue.
But I won't climb the tree just to see them,
For to frighten a robin won't do.

Of course, I will be very careful,
And look when the robins have gone.
To find fat, juicy bugs for their dinner,
Of some worms they pull out of the lawn.

A thing that I like about robins
Is the way that they hear the least sound.
Their tiny black heads turn and listen,
Then they pull that worm out of the ground.

A thing that I like about robins
Is the brave way they fight for their brood.
A snake and a cat are much bigger,
And they like baby robins for food.

But the robins drive off there intruders,
And they build a new nest closer by;
The babies sit weak and unsteady,
For, of course, they are learning to fly.

The mother and father will teach them
To come from the nest overhead,
By holding the bugs and worms toward them,
So the babies must come to be fed.

Soon the babies fly farther and farther,
From bushes to trees like the rest,
And each baby can then get its own food
While the mother sits on her new nest.

You might think she would be very tired
To feed a new brood right away,
For people have counted to say that
She makes hundreds of trips every day.

But the robins keep working and singing
Their songs from the shed-roofs and trees;
And every Spring day we can see them -
The whole family busy as bees.

Something to do and say: Bring in a discarded bird nest for display and discussion. Be sure to show a colorful robin picture. Suggest that children research materials by bringing in a book about birds from the library. Since this is a long poem, record it for listening. Eventually, children will learn part of a poem by simply listening. This is effective programming material. Present added information to the class as you would a story. Have further discussion.

Learning More About Robins

A robin is about ten inches long. It is a native American bird. The male has brown-orange-red feathers underneath and brown-gray upper parts. It has a black head. Its white throat is streaked with black. Its tail feathers are tipped with white. The mother robin is smaller and not so colorful. A robin is the state bird of three states: Connecticut, Michigan and Wisconsin. But robins can be found in many other states. In the Fall they fly south. In the Spring, they are the first to fly north.

Robins sing a beautiful song. They build nests from twigs, string, roots, grass, rags and paper. Mud is used to hold the nest together. The male often helps build the nest. The female lays 3 to 6 blue eggs. When the babies hatch, the father feeds them.

NAUGHTY BLUJAY

I knew that something was very near,
Else why would those peanuts disappear?
I put out a handful quietly
For a squirrel that lives up in our tree.
A bluejay came and quick as a streak,
He grabbed one peanut in his beak.
And then he flew down to the ground,
And covered it with leaves he'd found.
Then back again the bluejay flew
And took a peanut number two.
The bluejay then flew 'round the tree,
And took a peanut number three.
The bluejay wanting more and more
Flew down for peanut number four.
The bluejay hadn't had his fill
With number five clamped in his bill.
He spied me with his beady eyes,
And scolded me with loud, harsh cries.
But I was happy now because
I knew who the peanut pirate was.

(Louise Binder Scott, *Rhymes for Learning Times*. ©1984 by the T. S. Denison Co., Inc. Minneapolis, Minnesota 1984. "*The Peanut Pirate*.")

Something to do and say: Dramatize the poem. Ask: "Which bluejay do you want to be." Record the poem and play it back for discussion and evaluation. The poem can be played with action. Present added information for discussion.

Learning More About Bluejays

A bluejay has blue and white feathers and topknot of feathers on its head. It is a very bold and has a loud voice. Its voice is a loud shriek: "Thief, thief, thief." Sometimes its voice is soft and sounds like "Too-it." It is about twelve inches long from head to tail. Its under part is light gray. Around its throat is a collar of black feathers.

A bluejay is a beautiful bird. It will steal shiny things, but you can forgive it if it is bad. It eats the eggs of other birds. But it does eat harmful insects, acorns and nuts. The mother lays three to six greenish-looking eggs. Bluejays live about four or five years.

MOCKINGBIRD

A mockingbird once built a nest
Right near my windowsill.
A mocker never seems to rest
Perhaps it never will.

Children: Mockingbird, mockingbird,
Sings every song that it has heard.

It makes so many little flights
That don't go anywhere.
Its wings and tail are flashing white
When flying through the air.

Children: Mockingbird, mockingbird
Sings every song that it has heard.

It builds its nest - just any kind
Of things it can put in it -
Twigs, grasses, string - it does not mind.
It isn't still one minute.

Children: Mockingbird, mockingbird,
Sings every song that it has heard.

This bird sings songs of every kind
Of bird that flies in Spring -
Frogs, cats and other sounds it makes.
It copies everything!

Children: Mockingbird, mockingbird,
Sings every song that it has heard.

A mockingbird protects its young
And gives such loving care.
That sweetest songs on earth are sung
By that gray songbird there.

Children: Mockingbird, mockingbird,
Sings every song that it has heard.

Something to do and say: Suggest that individuals become mockingbirds and imitate a tune you or the children may hum. Record the poem and play it back for discussion. Present added information for the class. Ask how much children remember about the mockingbird so they can tell their families.

Learning More About Mockingbirds

A mockingbird can imitate other birds. That is why it is called a mockingbird. One person studied the mockingbirds's habits. She said that it imitated songs of 32 different birds. But it has a very sweet song of its own. It sings all year long and can somethimes be heard at night. It has a white breast and gray coat. Its tail and wings are darker gray. It has a long tail. It has a long thin bill. Females lay from three to five greenish-blue eggs in a cup-shaped nest. Some eggs are blue with brown spots. Mockers sometimes raise two families during the Summer. Babies hatch in about two weeks. They will attack anything or anybody that comes near their nests or territories.

THE WHIPPOORWILL

A whippoorwill has specks of white
On his feathers brown and gray.
He flies so quietly at night;
But he rests throughout the day.

Children: Whippoorwill, whippoorwill!
Sing your song, whippoorwill.

He sleeps so still for many hours
On a log or on a limb
Which is white and brown and gray,
And the limb looks just like him.

Children: Whippoorwill, whippoorwill!
Sleep awhile, whippoorwill.

He has soft, velvet, spotted wings
And funny whiskers on his bill
That help to catch bugs as he flies
And Whippoorwill will eat his fill.

All: Have you ever seen a Whippoorwill?
Oh, I hope some day you will!

Something to do and say: Ask what the class learned about the whippoorwill. Make up a tune for the refrain. Play it on the auto harp. Ask: "What kind of sound can you make to imitate the whippoorwill's song?" Present added information and discuss it.

Learning More About the Whippoorwill
When a whippoorwill sings, the song sounds like "whippoorwill." This bird lives in most parts of the United States and Canada. It is about ten inches long. It flies so quietly you cannot hear it. It opens its beak as it flies. The whiskers on its beak catch bugs as it swoops along. The female lays two violet and brown eggs among leaves. The nests are on the ground. Whippoorwills help farmers by eating harmful insects that can harm their crops.

46

SAY "HELLO" TO MISTER CROW

Oh, there's a very clever bird,
Whose name I'm sure you know.
He has shining, glossy feathers
And his name is Mister Crow.

Children: Caw, Caw, Caw,
And his name is Mister Crow!

Away up in our shady tree,
A special place he chose,
And helped his mate to build a nest
For five young baby crows.

Children: Caw, Caw, Caw,
For five young baby crows!

The mother crow sat on her eggs
She'd laid so carefully;
And Mister Crow helped keep them warm
To hatch the family.

Children: Caw, Caw, Caw,
To hatch a family!

Old Mister Crow lives on the farm,
And oh, he's very sly.
He'll steal the farmer's yellow corn,
Then flap his wings and fly.

Children: Caw, Caw, Caw,
Then flap his wings and fly.

The farmer says, "I do not care,
I like old Mister Crow.
If Mister Crow did not eat worms,
My fine crops would not grow."

Children: Caw, Caw, Caw,
               My fine crops would not grow.

               One day, I helped my mother hang
               The washing in the sun.
               Old Mister Crow came by and took
               A clothespin just for fun.

Children: Caw, Caw, Caw,
               A clothespin just for fun.

               When I leave shiny things around
               For Mister Crow to see,
               It's certain he will take them to
               His nest up in the tree.

Children: Caw, Caw, Caw,
               His nest up in the tree.

               Oh, there's a very clever bird,
               Whose name I'm sure you know.
               He has shiny, glossy feathers,
               And his name is Mister Crow.

Children: CAW, CAW, CAW!

Something to do and say: Arrange the poem for boys and girls, each group saying four lines. Practice with the tape recorder. Divide the group so they can practice with one another in a section of the room. Present added information as a story. Ask what individuals learned about the crow and write the responses to make a booklet. Show pictures of crows.

Learning More About Crows

The crow is a large black bird. It lives all over the world except in New Zealand. In the United States, we see crows in orchards, in meadows and in the woods. In Winter, crows fly south. A crow is about 18 inches long. It has a sharp beak and glossy, black feathers. There are some feathers on the tip of its beak. Its feet are strong. Crows do not have a song. They makes a noise. If caught when they are young, they make good pets. Sometimes they can be taught to talk. The female lays five or six eggs of bluish-gray with dark spots. Crows eat corn, and that is why the farmer makes a scarecrow. The scarecrow is dressed like a person and it scares away crows.

THE CHICKADEE

There is a black-capped chickadee
Sitting in our walnut tree.
The chickadee lives with her brood.
And all together find their food
Of insects, bugs and spider eggs.
She bathes in snow above her legs,
And cleans her feathers as she sings
She shakes her body and her wings.

Children: Chick-a-dee, chick-a-dee!
               I have great feathers! Look at me!

But, if she sees a cat around,
She makes a kind of buzzing sound.
At night, she finds the best of trees
And roosts with other chickadees.
Her body is a fluffy ball,
Tail hanging down, she looks so small;
And there she sleeps the whole night long,
At sunrise, you can hear her song.

Children: Chick-a-dee! Chick-a-dee!
               I am awake, as you can see!

She digs a hole to make her nest.
An old tree trunk she likes the best.
She lines it all with down and fur,
A very cozy place for her.
And on her seven eggs she'll sit.
She doesn't seem to mind a bit.
Because the father brings her food
'Til she can hatch the family brood.

Children: Chick-a-dee! Chick-a-dee!
               What a happy family!

Something to do and say: Ask children to tell what they learned from listening to the poem. Sometimes teachers record a poem and play the recording as the children are returning from recess to establish quiet. Present added information to the class.

Learning More About Chickadees

Chickadees go in a group to look for food. They call to one another as they fly from tree to tree. Their call sounds like "t-seep, t-seep." They spend most of their time eating and showing off their feathers. If a chickadee sees a hawk or a crow fly over, it will warm the others with a high, squeaky cry. The chickadees stay quiet until the danger is over.

Males and females sing a mating song: "Fee-bee, fee-bee" very loudly. When a chickadee makes a nest, both male and female poke with their bills in a dead stump. They carry away the chips so that an enemy won't know where the nest is hidden.

BEASTIES IN WOODS, MEADOW, PRAIRIE OR STREAM

LITTLE FAWN

Honey-colored little fawn
With polka dot trim -
His funny legs with tiny hoofs
Are wobbling under him.

His little ears are quick to hear.
He has such soft, brown eyes.
Though he was born six days ago,
He is so very wise.

A fawn learns fast at forest school
To hide and leap and run,
And hold his white tail in the air,
And kick his heels in fun.

He learns to find the tender leaves,
And grasses cool and sweet;
Although he has no upper teeth,
He does quite well to eat.

Two little knobs are on his head
Where antlers soon will sprout.
They're covered now with velvet skin.
By Fall, they will branch out.

His antlers drop, but he will grow
A bigger set each year,
Until he is a full-grown stag,
And graceful, white-tailed deer!

Something to do and say: Children tell what they learned about the fawn.
Pictures of deer and their young can be found in encyclopedias. Divide the poem
into parts for recording. Present added information to the class for discussion.

Learning More About Fawns

Female deer have one fawn the first time, and after that, each year she may have twins or even triplets. She licks the fawn's wet fur after it is born. When the fawn is an hour old, it can stand up. It follows its mother on its wobbly legs. She gives her baby milk. The mother licks her baby all over. Then it folds its legs under it and goes to sleep.

DEER IN THE SNOW

A deer came out of the forest
So cautiously I could see;
And right in a clearing near our house,
He steadily looked at me.

Children: Deer in the snow,
    Stay, don't go.

His eyes were so large and lovely;
His antlers like a dead limb
Would soon drop off and others would grow
A brand-new pair for him.

Children: Deer in the snow,
    Stay, don't go.

His sensitive nostrils quivered.
As I stood very still that day,
For one footstep would send him leaping,
And my deer would be frightened away.

Children: Deer in the snow,
    Stay! Please don't go!

Something to do and say: What kind of voice did you use when you asked the deer to stay? Say the line to show us. What does *cautiously* mean? *Sensitive*? Do you like these words? Why? Present added information.

Learning More About Deer

There are 60 kinds of deer; among them, mule, caribou, elk and moose. A deer is an animal with bones on its head. The bones are like horns with hard layers of skin. A deer runs from danger of wolves, coyotes and bears. It lives from 10 to 20 years.

RED SQUIRREL

All: Little Red Squirrel, I know what you are doing!
                       You are hiding some nuts for a cold winter's day.

Group 1:   When there's no food outside, you'll be happily chewing.
                       The good food you saved, when you hid it away.

All: Little Red Squirrel, I know why you are chattering!
                       You are angry at Gray Squirrel who chased you and tried

Group 2:   To steal all your treasures by tossing and scattering
                       The acorns and nuts that you wanted to hide.

All: Little Red Squirrel, your small whiskers are quivering.
                       You race up a tree and how quickly you sail!

Group 3:   When you jump between limbs, I can't keep from shivering
                       But, of course, you are helped by your parachute tail!

All: Little Red Squirrel, oh, why are you hurrying?
                       Your secret is out; at last I have guessed!

Group 4:   There are four baby squirrels, but you needn't start worrying,
                       I won't harm your babies. I won't touch your nest.

Something to do and say: Here is a chance to call attention to rhyming words. What rhymes with *doing*? with *day*? Use for programming. Let every volunteer have a turn. Say the poem using a different arrangement.

A TALE ABOUT A TAIL

A squirrel uses his tail for a balance,
When he jumps from limb to limb.
A tree is his home in the forest,
And nature is good to him.

His tail which is fluffy and furry,
He uses to clean up his room;
As he sweeps away all the nutshells
That tail makes a wonderful broom.

A squirrel's tail is a blanket
Which he uses to cover his nose,
As he curls the tail up all around him,
And sleeps while the winter wind blows.

Something to do and say: Discuss tails of other animals. Ask what children remember about the squirrel. Why did they like the poem? Have they seen squirrels? Tell of their experience. Would a squirrel make a good house pet? Why? Present added information for discussion.

LITTLE SQUIRREL

Just half way up in the walnut tree,
A bright-eyed squirrel is watching me,
And there beneath her on the ground,
Are shells of nuts that she has found.
She saves some nuts to hide away;
She will not eat them all today.
Now nuts, you know, are really seeds.
A squirrel hides more nuts than she needs.

Food that she hides, she may not find.
What happens if it's left behind?
The nut seed grows until you see
A giant oak or walnut tree!

(Louise Binder Scott, *Time for Phonics*, Book 3, McGraw-Hill Book Company, ©1968.)

Learning More About Squirrels

Like a rat, a squirrel is a rodent. It has big front teeth that gnaw. It can run 15 miles an hour. It has a very long bushy tail. There are many kinds of squirrels. Some are tiny and some are 12 inches long. Some live on the ground, and others in trees. They can jump from limb to limb for they have flaps of skin beside their bodies. Some squirrels are black. Others are gray or brown.

A red squirrel lives in northern United States and in Canada. It is very active. It is red and its lower parts are white. A black stripe runs along its side. It lives in trees. Nuts and grain are its foods. It often eats fruit, insects or bird's eggs.

The gray squirrel is larger than most squirrels. The mother has two to four babies. They are tiny with no hair. When an enemy comes, a gray squirrel can flatten its body on the limb of a tree and appear to hide. Like red squirrels, gray squirrels chatter.

ROLY-POLY PORCUPINE

Roly-poly porcupine,
The needles on your back
Are more than I can ever count,
And sharper than a tack.

Children: Roly-poly porcupine,
              Could you be a pet of mine?

You roll up in a cozy ball
When it is time to sleep.
Your tiny ears are very keen
To hear the smallest peep.

Children: Roly-poly porcupine,
              Could you be a pet of mine?

Oh my! Here comes a kitty-cat.
Look out! Oh, please take care!
A roly-ploy porcupine
Is resting over there!

Children: Roly-poly porcupine,
              Could you be a pet of mine?

Do not get near those needle quills.
They shoot up every one.
Kitty doesn't want to play.
Hurry! Run, run, run!

Children: I'm sorry Porky porcupine,
              That you can't be a pet of mine.

Something to do and say: Would you like a porcupine for a pet? Why? Why would a kitten be afraid of a porcupine? What kind of voice would you use to warn the kitty-cat? Present added information for discussion.

Learning More About Porcupines

The American porcupine is about 2 feet long. The tail is thick and is about 7 inches in length. The black quills are stiff hair, which are hollow spines that stand up. Porcupines eat plants only, such as buds, twigs and leaves. They gnaw their food. They live in dens. Young porcupines are born in the Spring. Porcupines are feared because they shoot their quills when afraid or angry. Some people eat porcupine flesh which is very fat.

MISCHIEVOUS LITTLE RACCOONS

There's a den in a tree with a hollow up high
And a mother and father raccoon were close by.
Inside were some young ones, I saw one, two, three
Curled up in round circles asleep in that tree.

Children: Intelligent, mischievous little raccoon,
                    Likes to explore by the light of the moon.

They had masks on their faces and rings 'round their eyes.
Like little black spectacles, looking so wise!
They had rings on their tails and their bodies were fat,
They looked all the world like the farmer's gray cat.

Children: Intelligent, mischievous little raccoon,
                    Likes to explore by the light of the moon.

And when I peeked closely, I saw on their feet,
Five fingers they use to wash food that they eat.
The babies came down and then every raccoon
Went out to explore by the light of the moon.

Children: Intelligent, mischievous little raccoon.
                    Likes to explore by the light of the moon.

They padded along on their baby-like feet
To the long river bank to find crayfish to eat.
They sat on their haunches and washed the food clean.
Preparing their fish made an interesting scene!

Children: Intelligent, mischievous little raccoon,
                    Likes to explore by the light of the moon.

They pried the clams open and took out the meat,
Then they washed once again and they nibbled their treat.
They went to the orchard, some peaches to steal,
For they needed dessert to finish their meal.

Children: Intelligent, mischievous little raccoon,
          Likes to explore by the light of the moon.

Each padded along in his little striped suit
So intelligent, mischievous, clever and cute!
But before daylight came, I knew they would be
Once more in their snug, hollow den in the tree.

Children: Intelligent, mischievous little raccoon,
          Likes to explore by the light of the moon.
(Louise Binder Scott, *Reading Skills*, McGraw-Hill Book Co., ©1972)

Something to do and say: Discuss the word *mischievous* which has three syllables, not four (mis'-chu-vus) and accented on the first syllable. Why would we say raccoons are mischievous? Ask if a raccoon would be a good pet? Why? Show pictures of raccoons. Ask what the class remembered from the poem. Present added information for discussion.

Learning More About Raccoons

A raccoon is about 32 inches long from nose to tip of tail. It weighs about 25 pounds. It is covered with long, coarse gray hair with black tips. It has grayish-white tail with black rings. There is a black patch around each eye with a ring of white around it. Raccoons have long legs and strong claws.

They eat frogs, turtles, crayfish and other animals that live in the water. They also like berries and fruits. They wash their food before they eat it. The bad things they do are raiding chicken coops and eating eggs. The female has from three to six babies in April or May. The babies are blind at birth. When they cry, they sound like real babies.

SLEEPY GROUNDHOG

Four drowsy groundhogs looked around, and around,
But they could not see any shadows on the ground.
Out of their holes, I saw them slowly climb.
It was February second and they knew that it was time.

> Said one, "I don't feel wide awake.
> I need a lot more rest and sleep."
> Said two, "The sky is gray and dark,
> Back to our hole I'd better creep."
> Said three, "I have a feeling that
> The sun will shine again quite soon."
> Said four, "I hope it hurries up.
> I'm sure that it is almost noon."
> "Hooray!" they shouted joyfully,
> With funny, lazy, little squeaks,
> "The sun has peeked out from the clouds,
> So we'll have six more sleepy weeks!"

Something to do and say: There are two lines for each pupil to say. Perhaps everyone can have a turn. Present added information for discussion. Find a picture of a groundhog to share with the class.

Learning About Groundhog Day

The custom of Groundhog Day came from England. People believed that the weather could be forecast for the next six weeks. The groundhog or woodchuck has a long sleep until February 2. Then he sticks his head out of the ground. He looks around to see if he can see his shadow. If he can see it, he goes back into his hole. This means that there will be six more weeks of winter. That statement has not been proved.

TOADS ARE TERRIFIC

Toads are quite gentle beasties.
They have such lovely eyes.
They have great, long and sticky tongues
That catch a bug that crawls or flies.

Toads are amphibians, of course;
They have gills like a fish.
They live in water and in fields
Toads are indeed most "cleverish."

All toads have terrible-looking warts
On legs, on heads, on backs.
The warts shoot out a poison
When a dangerous enemy attacks.

Some folks think warts are catching.
I know that is not true.
For you can touch toads anywhere.
Don't fear the toads. They won't harm you.

Something to do and say: Ask what information children learned about toads and tell if they have seen one and where. Bring in pictures of frogs and toads and discuss their differences. Present added information to the class for discussion.

Learning More About Toads

There are many kinds of toads. They are related to frogs, but spend more time on the land and have rougher and drier skin. Toads lay eggs and eat flies and other small insects. Toads do not have tails.

COTTONTAIL RABBIT

Girls: A cottontail has two large eyes
That look at you in round surprise.

Boys: At one glance, he sees everything -
A crow behind with spreading wings,

Girls: A squirrel above him on a limb,
A garter snake ahead of him.

Boys: A cottontail has two tall ears
That move to catch the sounds he hears,

Girls: And so to keep them extra keen,
He brushes them to keep them clean.

Boys: A cottontail has "sniffy" nose;
On his front feet he has five toes.

Girls: And four behind which help him jump.
His hind leg makes a great big thump!

Boys: Deep in a burrow he will hide,
And there he goes and stays inside.

Girls: His tail is just a cotton fluff
That looks like Mother's powder puff!

Something to do and say: These are only suggestions for dividing the poem. A line at a time could be said. After you have read the poem to the children, ask them what they remembered about the rabbit. Ask about experiences with rabbits. Would they make good pets? How would we take care of rabbits? Present added information for discussion.

Learning More About Rabbits
A rabbit is small and has very long ears. There are wild and tame rabbits. The tame ones can make fine pets. A tame rabbit digs a burrow. The babies are born with their eyes closed and they have no fur. Rabbits have a sharp edge on their upper front teeth.

One of the most interesting rabbits is the cottontail. It has a fluffy white underside to its tail. Cottontails weigh about three pounds. They like long grass and weeds where they can hide from enemies such as coyotes, wolves and bobcats. Cottontails usually come out at night. The mother may have from two to six babies. She may have several litters a year. Cottontails have strong legs that let them leap fast and far.

Something To Do

Cut white construction paper rabbit ears. Line with pink construction paper. Insert a pair of ears between a band of paper and close with a paper fastener to fit each child's head.

THE MUSKRAT

All: The muskrat is a clever beast
To build its house out in a pond.
From poles and piles of cattail sticks.
Of work, all muskrats are quite fond.

Group 1: Its tail is flat, its feet are webbed.
They help a muskrat swim about.
It digs a center in the house
So muskrats can go in and out.

Group 2: To plaster firmly, mud is used;
And weeds are piled on sides and top.
There is a platform where it sits
To eat a tasty cattail crop.

Group 3: And then when icy winter's gone,
The mother finds a place among
New cattails where she builds a nest
In Spring, prepared to have her young.

All: She may have babies four or twelve
But work is how she spends her days.
A muskrat is a clever beast;
It certainly deserves our praise.

Something to do and say: Ask the class what they remember about the muskrat from your reading the poem. Tape it and play it back for further listening. Ask children why a muskrat is clever. What does *clever* mean? Find pictures of muskrats. Present added information for discussion.

Learning More About Muskrats

Muskrats have sharp front teeth. They carry plant stalks, mainly cattails and twigs to a muddy place in the middle of a marsh. They pile up the stalks beneath the "house" and dig a burrow up into the center. When Winter arrives, they pile more cattails on top and sides until the walls are a foot thick.

LITTLE BROWN BAT

Little brown bat hanging upside-down,
Now it is time to awake,
The sun has gone down and so you must leave
Your snug hollow stump by the lake.

Children: Little brown bat, fly in the night.
Go home again when it is daylight.

Your baby will hold to your velvety fur
As you zig-zag and flutter and turn.
You will even swoop down for a drink in the lake,
And that's how your baby will learn.

Children: That's how your baby will learn.

You will spread your large wings as you fly through the night.
You look like a bird as you go.
Twisting and turning, you zig and you zag
To catch a mosquito below.

Children: You will catch a mosquito below.

You don't see too well, as you fly through the air,
But the highly-pitched sounds that you make
Bounce back like an echo and guide you so well,
You can't bump into things by mistake.

Children: Don't bump into things by mistake.

You squeak like a mouse as it runs through the house,
And some very shrill squeaks you can make,
But when daylight comes and the nighttime is gone,
You fly back to your home by the lake.

Children: Little brown bat, fly in the night.
Go home again when it is daylight.

Something to do and say: Read the poem. Ask the children to tell what they remember about the bat and her baby. What color was the bat? Where was its home? How will she take her baby to the lake? What does the bat eat? What kind of sound does it make? Does a bat fly by day or night? Read the poem again and ask the children to help you. When teaching to memorize, say part of a line (verse) and ask the class to complete it. Present the added information to the class.

Learning More About Bats

Most bats live in caves, attics or dark places of shelter. There are more than 900 species. Most of them hang upside-down when resting. All bats can see, but poorly. They are harmless but they may get rabies and a bat's bite can be dangerous. Bats have sharp teeth. The hands serve as wings. They eat half their weight in insects each day.

FRIENDLY SKUNK

All: Oh, friendly little creature
With your furry coat of black,
And snow-white stripe that goes along
Your tail and on your back.

Boys: Oh, could you be a kitten?
And can you say, "Meow?"
You remind me of a furry,
Baby kitten somehow.

Girls: "No, I am not a kitten
Although kittens are quite nice;
But I have a soft and feathery tail,
And I like to feed on mice!

Boys: I get drowsy in the winter
And into my burrow creep.
So there I lie on grass and leaves,
And sleep and sleep and sleep."

All: You friendly little animal,
You are a skunk, I'll bet.
If you took away your perfume
You would make a splendid pet!

Something to do and say: Use dramatization with children pretending to be a skunk and using his or her own words. Read the poem again and ask what they learned from the poem. Discuss rhyming words. Find a picture of a skunk. Present added information for discussion.

THE SKUNK THAT WANTED TO SING

The big brass gong went gong, gong, gong!
The bells went ding, ding, ding!
The skunk sat in a flower bed,
And cried, "I want to sing!"

He heard the bang of the big, round drums
All playing for the king.
The little skunk blinked back a tear
And cried, "I want to sing!"

"Don't cry," a wise owl told the skunk.
"Don't wish for such a thing.
Be thankful for your quietness.
Night creatures need not sing."

Learing More About Skunks
A skunk is a black and white furry mammal. It is a member of the weasel family. It is about the size of a cat with short legs and an arched back. It has a short tail. Near its tail are two scent liquid glands that give out a terrible odor. It is there to protect the skunk from enemies. A skunk that is scared can squirt the liquid up to ten feet. If its glands are removed, it makes a friendly pet.

Skunks are night animals. They sleep during the day. They live in hollow logs or dens. Skunks kill harmful insects, rats and mice.

Making Skunk Ears
Make skunk ears from doubled black construction paper. Glue a white stripe down the center of each ear. Double a strip of black construction paper. Insert the ears and glue them inside the strip. Fasten the strip together to fit the child's head.

THE SLY COYOTE

Girls: A slinking gray coyote
      With soft padded feet
      Came sniffing around
      For something to eat.

Boys: His sly, greedy eyes
      Looked sharply about.
      He spied rabbit tracks,
      And sniffed with his snout.

All: Slumpety, slump, slumpety, slump,
      Slumpety, slump, sniff, sniff!
      Slumpety, slump, slumpety, slump,
      Slumpety, slump, sniff, sniff!

Boys: Two furry jack rabbits
      With leaps and with bounds
      Were both jumping over
      Two prairie dog mounds.

Girls: The coyote jumped at them,
      And gave them a scare.
      He tried hard to catch them.
      Then hopped out of there.

All: A-plunker-hunk, a-plunker-hunk,
      A-plunker-hunk, who-oo-oo!
      A-pitty-pat, a-pitty-pat,
      A-pitty-pat, pa-too-oo!

(Adapted, unable to trace author.)

Something to do and say: Ask: "Did you like the sound of this poem? Why?" Help the children learn the third and last stanzas. Make up a tune to use with the last stanza. Which other animals were in the poem? Read the poem again and ask the children to count the animals named.

Learning More About The Coyote

It is a member of the dog family. It weighs about 30 pounds and is about 36 inches long including a 12 to 15 inch tail. It can run 40 miles an hour and it hunts chipmunks, rabbits and mice. It also eats berries and prickly pear cactus. It lives about 13 years.

The coyote's parents are mates for life. They have their babies in the spring and treat their babies with love and attention. At night, they serenade with howls and whines.

TAME BEASTIES

CATS, CATS, CATS!

All cats eyes shine when it is dark.
They sharpen claws on old tree bark.
They raise their backs when they are mad,
And purr to show you they are glad.

A cat's pink tongue is very rough;
Of course, it serves her well enough
For lapping milk and washing fur
That covers every part of her.

The Maltese cat has yellow eyes,
The Siamese has loudest cries;
But catnip pleases every cat
From alley to aristocrat.

Cats have some cousins at the zoo.
I know that we can name a few.
The lion cousin, grayish tan,
Is clearly not a friend of man.

The jaguar and the tiger bold
Are graceful creatures to behold.
No matter what the size or age,
These need a jungle or a cage.

Cats lived a million years ago,
As science and old fossils show.
No animal I've seen as yet
Could make a cleaner, finer pet.

Something to do and say: This poem is effective when line-a-child is used. Read
the poem again. Ask children to help by saying with you as many words as they
can and tell how many facts they can remember. When do cats eyes shine the
brightest? Of what use is a cat's tongue? Name as many kinds of cats as you can.
Ask "Why do cats make good pets? Do you have a pet cat? What kind? Describe
it. Where have you seen members of the cat family? How are all members of the

cat family the same? Which ones are dangerous? Which ones have you seen in the zoo? Find out if you can bring your pet cat to show us." Present added information to the children.

BABY KITTEN

When daytime hours begin to fade,
Baby Kitten, aren't you afraid?
The night is cloudy, no moon or star.
I hope you are not going far.
You are so small and so alone.
Shouldn't you wait until you are grown?
Said Baby Kitten, "But night is nice
For kittens and skunks and owls and mice.
Our eyes can see to lighten the way.
They do almost as well as during the day.
In the dark we enjoy just creeping around
And listening for every nighttime sound.
Our eyes are lamps that give excellent light
Whenever we're prowling in the dark night."

Something to do and say: Read the poem. On the second reading ask the class to try to supply the rhyming word in each couplet, then on a second reading, ask them to say as much of the poem as they can with you. Make a cat puppet as represented here. Use a lunch bag. Draw a cat's face. Use pipe cleaners for whiskers.

Learning More About Cats
Cats have been tame for thousands of years. They were originally used to catch mice and rats rather than considered as pets. There are many different breeds and types of domestic cats. Lions, tigers, lynx and leopards are also cats. Domestic cats can live to 14 years old and can weigh as much as 20 pounds. Some cats have blue eyes, some are green and others are gray. Their fur can be white, yellow or gray. They may also have stripes or be many colors.

DOGS WE KNOW

Dogs would say words if they but could,
Yet they can all be understood.
A dog yaps when she sits and begs.
She tucks her tail between her legs -
She is ashamed when she's been bad.
She hangs her head when she is sad.
When she is angry, she will growl,
When she is lonely, she will howl.
She wags her tail and likes to race,
Play tag with me, and lick my face.
But here is one thing I should mention:
All dogs want love and need attention.
My dog can't talk, you will agree,
But she communicates with *me*!

Something to do and say: Suggest a discussion about dogs. "Do you have a pet dog? Are all dogs good pets? Why? What kinds of dogs are there? Are some useful? (Seeing-eye) In what way? How does one care for a dog? Where do we keep it? Tell about laws concerning dogs. How would you identify a dog if it were lost?" Present added information for discussion.

Learning More About Dogs

Dogs are the oldest tame animal in America. Indians had dogs when white men came to this country. White men brought dogs with them. Dogs are related to wolves and jackals. Dogs are used to hunt birds and foxes. Some are watch dogs or "seeing eye dogs" that help the blind. Some herd sheep or cattle and goats. Some pull a sled in Alaska. Most of all, dogs make wonderful pets. They can be trained. They are very affectionate and are great companions. Look in the encyclopedia to find the number of breeds.

MY HAMSTER

Group 1:   My hamster has soft golden fur
                    That covers every part of her.

Group 2:   My hamster is so neat and clean,
                    And she is friendly, never mean.

Group 3:   My hamster runs around at night,
                    And then she rests when it is light.

Group 4:   My hamster has a baby brood,
                    And in her cheeks she carries food.

Group 5:   My hamster has soft, little paws,
                    She uses sharp teeth when she gnaws.

Group 6:   My hamster has a running wheel.
                    If I ran that fast, I would feel

All: DIZZY!

Something to do and say: Take the class to a pet shop to observe pets. You may want to borrow a hamster for your classroom. How would you take care of a hamster? Describe one.

Learning More About A Hamster
Hamsters are rodents that originally came from Europe and Asia. They have white and gold fur. Hamsters have long tails and very large cheeks that they use to store and carry food. They are small enough to fit in your hand and can live happily in a very small space. Hamsters are mammals.

PARAKEET

Group 1:   A parakeet, so I have been told
                    Can be trained to talk when a few weeks old.

Group 2:   Its hearing is keen, and I have heard
                    It is taught to say almost any word.

Group 3:   Its tail can be short or it can be long.
                    It's a beautiful pet but it can't sing a song.

Group 4:   It's a most clever acrobat, curiously quick
                    With a seesaw or ladder or other such trick.

Group 5:   It likes seeds and fruits, and you can just bet
                    That it's an affectionate, clever bird pet.

All: My family of pets would be complete,
                    If someone would give me a parakeet.

Something to do and say: Take a trip to a pet shop to see a parakeet. Describe one. Have you seen a parakeet? Where? Why is it a clever bird to have as a pet? Present added information to the class for discussion.

Learning More About a Parakeet

They are affectionate and clever. They are sometimes called *budgies*. Both the male and female can learn words. The female may lay an average of five eggs and they will hatch in about 18-20 days. The parakeet lives about ten years. Colors are orange, green, yellow, red, blue and purple. Tails are short, square or pointed. To teach it to talk, start when it is very young and repeat a word or phrase over and over.

75

MRS. DUCK

Mrs. Duck said, "I don't need
Umbrellas for rain.
I'm in luck if the sun
Doesn't come out again.

My ducklings and I like
The rumble of thunder.
I need no umbrella
That I must hide under.

I enjoy the mud puddles,
The lovely rain makes.
When I'm hungry, I dive
For my lunch in the lake."

THE DUCK FAMILY

Ducks and drakes like rainy weather.
They are happier wet than dry;
Drops fall off of all their feathers
Which are oily, that is why.

Ducks and drakes are joyful fellows
When their quacking serenade,
Followed by their ducklings yellow,
They make quite a dress parade.

Ducklings are such loving creatures
With their soft and downy backs.
Among the baby's nicest features
Are its flat feet and its quacks.

Something to do and say: Ask if a duck would make a good pet? in the city? on a farm? What care would a duck need? Find a book with duck pictures. Draw one. Describe a duck; it's baby duckling. Present added information for discussion. Say the poem all together with the teacher.

Learning More About Ducks

Ducks like water. We know that. People sometimes say, "This is fine weather for ducks." Duck's feet are not like chicken's feet. They have webs to help the ducks paddle. When ducks dive, they kick with their webbed feet. Their feet drive them down in the pond where there are bugs and insects. The mother is called a duck. The father is a drake. The babies are ducklings.

PETS I WOULD LIKE

Child 1:   I would like a baby duckling
                  That has a friendly quack.

Child 2:   Or perhaps a frisky pony
                  That will take me on its back.

Child 3:   I might like a hungry pelican
                  That eats all it can hold.

Child 4:   Or perhaps a gorgeous peacock
                  Clad in blue and green and gold.

Child 5:   I would like that furry rabbit
                  In its burrow on the hill.

Child 6:   And I'm sure I'd like a puffin
                  With its very curious bill.

Child 7:   I wish I had a goldfish
                  That swims inside a bowl,

Child 8:   Or perhaps a harmless gartersnake,
                  Or a velvety, soft mole.

All: I will settle for a puppy
                  Or just any pet, you see,
                  As long as I can choose it,
                  And it belongs to ME!

Something to do and say: Ask which choice of pet the child would like. Individuals may say one or two lines. Record the poem for discussion. Which pets are not mentioned. Suggest that children dictate a sentence about their pets. Write the sentence for a booklet. Look for pictures of the pets, particularly ones with which children might be unfamiliar: *puffin, peacock, pelican, gartersnake.*

ZOO BEASTIES

HUGE HIPPOPOTAMUS

The "hippo" is huge and resembles a hog.
She has quite a heavy, thick hide.
A "hippo" can weigh all of 8000 pounds.
She is small-eared and also small-eyed.

Children: Hippo, hippopotamus,
                Hardly ever makes a fuss.

She has bristles for hair on her head, neck and tail;
Her big hoof has only four toes,
She stays under water a very long time.
And she spouts water out of her nose.

Children: Hippo, hippopotamus,
                Hardly ever makes a fuss.

A "hippo" is clumsy and bulky and slow.
She never could win in a race.
A "hippo" is brown or she may be blue-gray,
With a big smile all over her face.

Children: Hippo, hippopotamus,
                Hardly ever makes a fuss.

Something to do and say: Ask if the children have seen a hippopotamus and where. Would it make a good pet? Why? Present added information for discussion.

Learning More About Hippopotamuses

We can see a hippopotamus at the zoo. Next to the elephant, it is the heaviest of all animals. It can weigh 8000 pounds. It has four short legs. Each foot has four toes. "Hippos" lie flat on the ground. The "hippo" has a huge mouth. It can open 3 or 4 feet. It's teeth are long and strong. The skin on a "hippo's" body can be an inch and a half thick. It swims well. It can stay under water for ten minutes. The female has only one baby at a time. She teaches it to swim. A "hippo" can live for about 30 years.

THE CAMEL

The camel has a bumpy back
Instead of one that's flat.
And yet folks take a ride on her!

Children: Now, what do you think of that?

A camel has a scornful face.
She's an aristocrat.
But, please don't judge her by her looks.

Children: Now, what do you think of that?

She has a tummy like a tank -
Holds water like a vat.
She travels miles without a drink.

Children: Now, what do you think of that?

Something to do and say: Ask "What do you know about camels? What is an *aristocrat*? Let's look up the meaning. Have you seen a camel. Where?" Present added information for discussion. Ask how many would like to ride a camel. Why?

Learning More About Camels

The camel has been called "The Ship of the Desert." It is mentioned in the Bible. A camel is awkward and humpbacked with a neck like a goose. A camel can have one or two humps on its back. There are millions of camels in the world. Some live in Arabia, India or Africa. A camel drinks 30 gallons of water in minutes. It does not perspire as we do. The eyes of a camel have heavy eyelids and long eyelashes. It has a big upper lip and strong, yellow teeth. It has two broad toes on its feet and they keep the camel from sinking in sand. A camel can live 40 years and is not full-grown until it is 17.

THE ELEPHANT

An elephant has a trunk so long
She can't use it to bite.
And yet she'll eat a bale of hay
With a great, big appetite.
Her trunk can lift me in the air.
I do not mind at all.
She is so gentle with me and
I know I will not fall.

Something to do and say: Ask "Have you seen an elephant? Where? Would you like to ride one?" Find a picture of one. Somethimes elephants are seen in the circus. Have you been to a circus? Tell about it. Perhaps you can learn the poem so we can record it. Present added information for discussion.

Learning More About Elephants

We have all seen an elephant at the zoo or in a circus. It is the largest animal in the world and the second tallest. A giraffe is the tallest. An elephant has very large ears that look like big fans. It is the only animal that has a nose which is in the form of a trunk. It uses the trunk as a hand to pick up food to put into its mouth. Sometimes it has big tusks. Some elephants have no tusks. An elephant eats leaves, fruit, grass and roots. It lives about sixty years. You know that an elephant is very intelligent. It can be trained to lie down or dance or do tricks. We all like elephants for they are gentle creatures. Look on a globe and find Africa, Thailand and China, where elephants are found.

RHINOCEROS

I've seen a rhinoceros, have you?
I saw a rhinoceros at the zoo.
Though he's related to a horse;
You cannot ride on him of course.

Children: Keep away from a rhinoceros.
He is sure to make a lot of fuss.

He has four feet and heavy toes.
He has a horn stuck in his nose.
And he can run quite fast, they say
So you should keep out of his way!

Children: Keep away from a rhinoceros.
He is sure to make a lot of fuss.

He rams a car up in the air
Till it is gone - beyond repair!
No telling what this beast will do.
Be sure he keeps away from you.
Whenever you go to the zoo!

Something to do and say: Ask where children have seen a rhinoceros and to describe one. Find a picture. Present added information for discussion.

Learning more About the Rhinoceros

It takes about 19 months for a mother to have her baby. The baby may weigh 50 pounds (22kg) and stand about 20 inches high. An hour after birth, the baby can stand. It stays close to its mother for as long as two to four years. A rhinoceros is a huge animal. It has short legs and its skin hangs loosely on its body. It has almost no hair. Sometimes a "rhino" has one or two curved horns that come out of its nose. It has three toes on each foot. It has one toe that did not develop.

A rhinoceros eats grass and shrubs. It also likes the food we eat. There are several kinds of rhinoceros. Some of them are six feet tall. A "rhino" hide hangs in big folds and is very thick.

AN APE

An ape has arms and legs like me,
But has a larger shape.
His skull is thick, his brain is small.
When trying to escape,
He leaps from branches of a tree
And goes at greatest speed.
I wouldn't care to catch an ape,
Or tame him, no indeed!
Most of the time he's at the zoo
Sometimes he's in a rage.
He gives me such an ugly look,
And shakes bars of his cage.
But as I watch him at the zoo,
I'm sure he thinks I'm funny, too!

Something to do and say: Ask: "What did you learn from hearing the poem? I will read it more than once. Perhaps you can help me. Why would an ape think you are funny?" Present added information for discussion.

Learning More About Apes

Apes can be gorillas, chimpanzees, orangutans and gibbons. Apes resemble monkeys for their heads and necks are similar. The ape lives in a tropical forest. We can see them in zoos.

DON'T POKE A CROCODILE
A Poem for Fun

If you should meet a crocodile
    Don't wake him up and poke.
Pay no attention to his smile,
    He doesn't like a joke.
A crocodile sleeps in the Nile
    Just listen to your hunch.
Remember that this beast may be
    Inspecting you for lunch!

Something to do and say: Ask the children to locate the Nile River on a map. Can you see a crocodile in the United States? Why should you be careful of them? Would you have one for a pet? Why? Let's find a picture of a crocodile. Draw a picture of one. Learn the poem and say it for your family and friends.

CROCODILE

A long, old lazy crocodile lay sleeping in the sun.
The sky was blue, the day was warm,
And he was having fun.
The sand was hot and he liked that.
His throat was getting dry.
He stretched - Ho-hum! He smacked his jaws
And blinked one sleepy eye.
He saw some sparkling water and he sidled to the bank.
The water trickled down his throat.
He drank and drank and drank!

Something to do and say: How would you say the poem about a crocodile? With an angry voice? a sleepy voice? a sad voice? a happy voice? Why? Pretend to be a crocodile. Tell what you like to do.

Learning More About Crocodiles
    A crocodile is found in North and South America and in Africa in tropical climates. It can be as long as 15 feet and as small as 3 feet. It has 22 teeth in each jaw. It has short legs and scaly skin and its tail is dangerous. Crocodiles are good swimmers. They eat birds, turtles, fish and even large animals. They lay eggs and live about 30 years.

AN AARDVARK

Group 1:   An aardvark's tongue is very long.
             On ants an aardvark likes to munch;

Group 2:   And termites are a favorite dish
             For breakfast, dinner and for lunch.

Group 3:   An aardvark has an ugly snout.
             His tail is long. His teeth are big.

Group 4:   It is indeed unfortunate
             He can't be handsome as a pig.

Group 5:   He has no special talents and
             An aardvark isn't clever, very.

All: His name begins with a double *a*,
             He's first in every dictionary!

Something to do and say: Look up aardvark in the dictionary. Does it lead other words that begin with *a*? Let's find a picture of an aardvark. Would you have one for a pet? Why? Look in your dictionary to see if the word *aardvark* is at the top of the list of "*a*" words.

Learning More About Aardvarks

In 1600, Dutch settlers in Africa gave the aardvark its name. The word means "earth pig." An aardvark is four to six feet long from tip to snout to tip of tail. It weighs over 130 pounds. Its ears resemble those of a donkey. Tongues can be 18 inches long. It sleeps during the day and looks for food at night.

PRIM PENGUINS

Penguins march in even rows
Dressed in smart, crisp evening clothes.
Majestic, dignified and prim.
Every penguin looks so trim.
I wish that we were half so keen
On keeping clothing spotless clean!

Something to say and do: Let's learn and record this poem. Find a picture of a penguin. Do you like penguins? Why? Could you have one for a pet? Why? Discuss words: *majestic, dignified and prim*.

Learning More About Penguins
Penguins cannot fly, but they are excellent swimmers. They have scalelike feathers, flipper shaped wings and webbed feet. Penguins live in the cool regions of the Southern Hemisphere. Penguins like to eat fish, squid, shrimp, clams and lobsters.

FUZZY KOALA

All: I like my little Koala friend, he looks just like a bear.
            I could hold him every day! Koala wouldn't care.
            Tell us why you have a funny, rubber, button nose.

Child 1:   My nose is most important for I follow where it goes.

All: Tell us why your ears are bigger than the rest of you.

Child 2:   Because big ears are needed for the things I listen to.

All: Tell us why you have no tail, or don't you really care.

Child 3:   I cannot say. I guess it's 'cause nobody put it there.

All: I like my little Koala friend, he looks just like a bear.
            I could hold him every day. Koala wouldn't care.

(Adapted: from a poem by Conrad Wedberg; *Talking Time*, Louise Binder Scott and J. J. Thompson, copyright by authors.)

Something to say and do: Ask: "Was the poem fun? Why?Let's find a picture of a Koala. How is it different from other bears? I will tell you more about our little friend..."

Learning More About the Koala

The Koala is not a bear! It is a member of the same family as the kangaroo, called marsupials. This means it has a pouch where Koala babies will live until they have grown large enough to survive in the world like its parents. He is covered with bluish-gray hair, has a rubbery nose and fluffy ears. The Koala is two to three feet long and weighs about three pounds. The Koala is considered full grown in four years and can live for twenty. A Koala lives on eucalyptus leaves and buds. This is the only food it ever eats. It has a baby every other year.

KANGAROO

1. Old hoppity, loppity kangaroo
    Can jump much higher than me or you.

2. Her tail is a weapon and very strong.
    And it helps her leap as she travels along.

3. And when she jumps, she uses her tail,
    So she can fly high and almost sail.

4. She carries her baby inside her pouch,
    Which is far more comfortable than your couch.

5. Old hoppity, loppity kangaroo,
    Hoppity, loppity, jump one-two!

Something to say and do: You may want to use this as a "jump rope" rhyme. Ask children if they have seen a real kangaroo and where. Present added information for discussion.

Learning More About Kangaroos

Kangaroos are large animals about 6 feet tall. The tail is long and very heavy and it is used to help the kangaroo keep its balance and speed over the ground at 25 miles an hour on level ground. Its fur is soft. It has a head about the size of a sheep, dark brown eyes and round ears. The babies live in the mother's pouch for about 6 months. A baby is called a "*joey*."

THE DUCKBILL PLATYPUS

A platypus is strange as strange can be,
She's like nothing you ever have seen.
Her leathery bill is shaped like a duck.
She's a "freak," if you know what I mean.

Children: Funny Duckbill Platypus,
I wish that you would visit us.

She lives in Australia across the wide sea.
The way she is made is all wrong.
She is covered with fur and she cannot say "quack."
She just doesn't seem to belong.

Children: Funny Duckbill Platypus,
I wish that you would visit us.

She lays two or three eggs not over an inch;
And she curls her long body around
Until the eggs hatch and the babies appear.
Her song is a soft snoring sound.

Children: Funny Duckbill Platypus,
I wish that you would visit us.

A Duckbill creeps forward and backward as well.
When angry, she never will fight.
On her claw is a poisonous fang to defend
Which she uses with all of her might.

Children: Funny Duckbill Platypus,
I wish that you would visit us.

She is neither a duck or a beaver or fish.
She doesn't belong anywhere.
But she is a beautiful creature to see.
Let's protect her because she is rare.

Children: Funny Duckbill Platypus,
I wish that you would visit us.

Something to say and do: What did you learn about a Duckbill Platypus? Find a picture of a Duckbill Platypus in the encyclopedia. What does it look like to you?

Learning More About The Duckbill Platypus

The duckbill platypus lives along streams in Australia. It likes to spend its time in the water, but it is an egg-laying mammal. There are only two mammals that lay eggs; the duckbill platypus and the echidna. A duckbill digs burrows on the banks of streams and blocks the entrance with leaves, grass and dirt. It grows from 16-22 inches and weighs about 5 pounds. There are no duckbills in the United States.

TIGER

1:   There's a tiger at the zoo, at the zoo;

2:   His stripes go up and down,

3:   And his stripes are black and orange

All: At the zoo!

4:   The tiger's in a cage at the zoo;

5:   And the cage is big and stout,

6:   So he never does come out,

7:   And he has a dish of water,

All: At the zoo!

8:   When the tiger wants his dinner at the zoo,

9:   The keeper hears him roar, and he opens up the door,

10: And he give him meat to eat

All: At the zoo!

11: Oh, the tiger has a grin upon his chin at the zoo,

12: And he whiffles with his nose, and he washes off his toes,

13: And he jumps upon a shelf and goes to sleep

All: At the zoo!

(From the book *Stories to Begin On* by Rhoda W. Bachmeister, © 1940, by E. P. Dutton & Co., Inc, New York, New York. Reprinted in *Learning Time: With Language Experiences for Young Children* by Louise Binder Scott, by permission of the author.)

Something to say and do: Ask "Have you seen a tiger? Where? Could you have one for a pet? Why? How is a tiger different from a lion. Let's find a pictue of both and compare them." Present added information for discussion.

Learning More About Tigers

A tiger belongs to the cat family. It lives in Asia and at our zoo. It is a very strong animal but not as strong as a lion. All tigers have black stripes on the head, body, legs and tail. It has a white dot over each eye. A male tiger may weigh 500 pounds (227 kg) and may be 5 feet tall. It has no mane like a male lion. Tigers are good swimmers. A mother tiger may have 2 to 6 cubs.

WINTER AT THE ZOO

I have a pair of zipper boots,
And zipper jacket, too.
I zip them up and go to see
The zebra at the zoo.

Children: At the zoo,zoo,zoo!
The zebra at the zoo.
Her stripes that zig-zag up and down
Are wound and wound
Around, around
The zebra at the zoo!

The zebra does not seem to mind
The zero air outside,
Because she's dressed for winter cold
In warm and furry hide.

Children: At the zoo,zoo,zoo!
The zebra at the zoo.
Her stripes that zig-zag up and down
Are wound and wound
Around, around
The zebra at the zoo!

Something to say and do: Ask: "Have you seen a zebra? Where? Describe a zebra. Would you ride on a zebra? Why?" Children say the refrain with you. They may want to make up a "zebra tune."

Learning More About Zebras

A zebra looks much like a horse except that it has black up and down stripes on the neck and body and circular stripes on the hind legs. It has long ears. Stripes are not always the same on zebras. The mother zebra has her baby in eleven to thirteen months. Zebras have never been tame.

PAINTING ZOO ANIMALS

If I could paint a tall giraffe,
(he's such a curious fellow)
I'd climb a ladder and I'd paint
Him lovely, golden yellow.

If I could paint an elephant,
And do it just my way,
I'd paint her body, ears and all
A beautiful, soft gray.

If I could paint a monkey
That is acting like a clown,
I'd paint her all from face to tail,
A velvet, autumn brown.

If I could paint a zebra
with stripes along her back,
I'd paint her first a snowy white
And add some stripes of black.

If I could paint a jungle snake
I think that would be keen
To paint him purple, pink and blue,
And orange and red and green!

Something to do and say: Children will delight in painting their own color versions of animals.

94

A TRIP TO THE ZOO

All: When we are on a holiday,
        What do you think we'll do?
        We'll get into a yellow bus,
        And we'll go to the zoo!

Child 1:   We like the little monkeys best.
            We like the way they jump.

Child 2:   They climb up with their hands and feet,
            And sometimes fall ker-plunk!

Child 3:   The giraffe with his great, long neck
            That stretches up so high -

Child 4:   It reaches top leaves in a tree,
            And seems to touch the sky.

Child 5:   The elephant is big and strong.
            We watch what he can do.

Child 6:   He gives a great loud bellow.
            And he waves his trunk at you.

All: The sea lion lies beside a pool.
        He looks around to see
        If someone's coming with his fish
        This afternoon for tea.

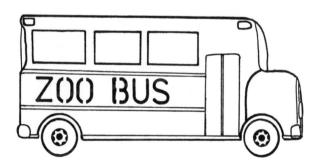

Something to say and do: Individual children tell what they would do if they visited the zoo. They tell what they have done. Which other animals would they see? Which animal is the funniest? Why? Which animal is your favorite? Why?

Beastie

Games

PANTOMIMING ANIMAL BEASTIES

A is for *ape* with a fierce, ugly face.   *(Make face.)*

B is for *bug* that runs every place.   *(Moves fingers rapidly.)*

C is for *colt* with long, nimble legs.   *(Trot in one place.)*

D is for *dog* that sits up and begs.   *(Kneel and place palms of hands together.)*

E is for *eagle* that flies in the sky.   *(Motion of flying.)*

F is for *fox* that is hungry and sly.   *(Move corners of mouth and eyes to left.)*

G is for *goat* that gallops around.   *(Take a galloping step.)*

H is for *horse* with a whinnying sound.   *(Whinny.)*

I   is for *insect* that bites and it stings.   *(Slap hands.)*

J is for *jay* with flashing blue wings.   *(Pretend to fly.)*

K is for guess - why, of course, *kangaroo.*   *(Make leap in air.)*
You can see in Australia or at our own zoo.

L is for *lizard* so slippery and quick.   *(Move hand back and forth.)*

M is for *mule* that may give a swift kick.   *(Kick foot backward.)*

N is for *nightingale's* songs that are sweet.   *(Whistle.)*

O is for *ostrich* with very strong feet.   *(Stamp foot.)*

P is for *pig* so fat and so round.   *(Make circle with arms and puff out cheeks.)*

Q is for *quail* with a nest on the ground.   *(Cup hands.)*

R is for *rabbit*, a fine pet for me.   *(Place pointer fingers beside head).*

S is for *seal* that swims in the sea.   *(Make swimming motion.)*

T is for *tiger* with stripes on its back.   *(Draw lines in air.)*

U is for *umbrella bird* that is black.   *(Hands clasped over head.)*

V is for *vulture*. I don't want to see twice.   *(Cover face.)*

W is for *walrus* that lives on the ice.   *(Hug body.)*

X I am stuck! Alas and alack!   *(Extend hands.)*

Y is one beastie that we call a *yak*.   *(Move hands up for tallness.)*

Z is for *zebra* with stripes that are black.   *(Draw stripes in air.)*

RIDDLES ABOUT BIRD BEASTIES

Read the sentence at the left. Children supply the answer verbally.

1. Which bird has eyes that cannot move? *(owl)*

2. Which bird can fly backward? *(hummingbird)*

3. Which bird pecks on trees? *(woodpecker)*

4. Which bird has a nest on the ground? *(whippoorwill)*

5. Which bird has a loud, shrieking voice? *(bluejay)*

6. Which bird sings other birds' songs? *(mockingbird)*

7. Which bird likes to show off its feathers? *(chickadee)*

8. Which bird hunts for food at night? *(owl)*

9. Which bird has a pretty song? *(robin)*

10. Which bird is the smallest one in the world? *(hummingbird)*

11. Which bird says, "caw, caw?" *(crow)*

MORE RIDDLES

How can fish tell how much they weigh? *Answer:* They have their own scales.

What deer is the wettest animal? *Answer:* A reindeer.

If you had five ducks and put them in a box, what would you have? *Answer:* A box of quackers (crackers).

If a little bird found an orange in its nest, what would it say? *Answer:* Look at the orange marmalade! (Mama laid).

What is a sleepy bull called? *Answer:* A bulldozer.

What bee can't fly or sting? *Answer:* a spelling bee.

How did the flea get home for Thanksgiving? *Answer:* By Greyhound.

Why did the elephant stand on the marshmallow? *Answer:* Because he didn't want to fall into the hot chocolate.

Why would you tickle a mule? *Answer:* You'd get a big kick out of it.

Why did the mouse say, "Bow-wow-wow?" *Answer:* She was trying to teach her children a new language.

Why do hummingbirds hum? *Answer:* Because they can't remember the words.

Why did the boy think his dog was smart? *Answer:* When he asked, "What is two minus two," the dog said nothing.

Why did two crows sit on the telephone wire? *Answer:* They wanted to make a long-distance caw (call).

Why did the fly fly? *Answer:* Because the spider spider (spied her).

Children try to answer the riddles. Later, invite a child to "be the teacher" and ask them. Encourage the class to make up its own riddles about beasties.

MATCHING BEASTIE GAME

The children match words on the left with words on the right orally. Encourage the use of a complete phrase. *A fat hippopotamus. A growling bear. Honey bees.*

1. Striped -- zig-zag	1. Squirrel
2. Fat	2. Bees
3. Bushy-tailed	3. Skunk
4. Black and white	4. Firefly
5. Growling	5. Ladybug
6. Honey	6. Bear
7. Flickering	7. Hummingbird
8. Screech	8. Hippopotamus
9. Spotted	9. Owl
10. Humming	10. Zebra

ANIMAL QUIZZES

Children answer the question.

Which animal is a baby deer?   (fawn)

Which animal makes shrill squeaks
and lives in a tree stump of cave?   (bat)

Which animal has a tail like Mother's powder puff?   (rabbit)

Which animal has a strange perfume?   (skunk)

Which animal has a bushy tail?   (squirrel)

Which animal is mischievous and has five
fingers on its hand?   (raccoon)

Which animal sleeps all winter?   (bear or groundhog)

Which animal has needles or quills on its back?   (porcupine)

Which animal is an amphibian?   (toad)

CHOICES

Say the three words. The children select the correct word orally.

Which one has wings?	bear-cat-hen
Which one can you ride?	butterfly-camel-fish
Which one eats bugs?	grasshopper-goat-groundhog
Which one builds a nest?	skunk-robin-pig
Which one gives milk?	canary-crow-cow
Which one has a shrill voice?	bluejay-rabbit-mosquito
Which one has a shell on its back?	turtle-toad-woodpecker
Which one makes honey?	cricket-bee-dog
Which one sleeps all winter?	groundhog-"hippo"-bee

Write the names of some "beasties" on a chart and suggest that children make up their own game of choices.

WHAT THE ABC's DID

A asked an alligator.

B bumped into a bear.

C called a cat.

D discovered a dog.

E eyed an elephant.

F found a fish.

G got a goat.

H hunted a horse.

I ignored an iguana.

J jumped at a jack rabbit.

K kissed a kangaroo.

L led a lion.

M met a mule.

N noticed a newt.

O observed an octopus.

P petted a pig.

Q quieted a quail.

R roped a rabbit.

S saw a seal.

T touched a toad.

U upset an umbrella bird.

V viewed a vulture.

W watched a woodchuck.

X excited an ox.

Y yelled at a yak.

Z zeroed in on a zebra.

The children can no doubt think of other verbs and animals beginning with the alphabet letters. Explain that words beginning with *x* often have the "z" sound, in *xylophone* or begin with "short e" as in *ex* in *x-ray*.

CAN YOU MATCH THEM?

1. Mocking	1. Duck
2. Furry	2. Bullfrog
3. Pecking	3. Bird
4. Mischievous	4. Camel
5. Croaking	5. Dog
6. Humpy	6. Woodpecker
7. Purring	7. Owl
8. Barking	8. Rabbit
9. Quacking	9. Cat
10. Hooting	10. Racoon

The children complete orally the verb on the left with the word on the right. Read the test once or twice so that the children will have fun with matching. Examples: *Hooting owl, Hopping rabbit. Humpy camel.*

BEASTIE PUZZLE WORDS

Write the incomplete names of birds, animals and insects on the board. Omit vowels: *a, e, i, o* and *u*. Retain "*y*" even though it is used as a vowel at the end of a word. Use this exercise with second, third or older grades. Write the completed words and cover them until the children are ready to check their puzzles.

Insects

f _ r _ fly   cr _ ck _ t   dr _ g _ nfly

b _ tt _ r _ ly   gr _ ssh _ pp _ r   l _ dyb _ g

d _ ddy l _ ngl _ gs   _ ns _ ct   m _ sq _ _ t _

Birds

scr _ _ ch _ wl   sp _ rr _ w   h _ mm _ ngb _ rd

bl _ _ j _ y   c _ n _ ry   w _ _ dp _ ck _ r

r _ b _ n   m _ ck _ ngb _ rd   cr _ w

Animals in Field, Wood and Stream

f _ wn   r _ bb _ t   sq _ _ rr _ l   p _ rc _ p _ n _

b _ t   sk _ nk   r _ cc _ _ n   m _ skr _ t

b _ llfr _ g b _ _ r   gr _ _ ndh _ g   t _ _ d

Zoo

h _ pp _ p _ t _ m _ s   c _ m _ l   _ l _ ph _ nt

k _ ng _ r _ _   _ _ rdv _ rk   rh _ n _ c _ r _ s

Tame Beasties

c _ t   d _ g   h _ n   d _ ck   c _ w

g _ _ t   t _ rtl _   h _ mst _ r p _ ny   p _ g

BIBLIOGRAPHY

AARDVARK
Caple, Kathy - *Inspector Aardvark And The Perfect Cake*: Windmill Inc., Old Tappan, NJ, ©1980.
Higman, Jon Atlas - *Aardvark's Picnic*; Little Brown & Company, Boston, ©1986.

APE/GORILLA
Armour, Richard - *All Sizes And Shapes Of Monkeys And Apes*; McGraw-Hill Book Company, NY, © 1970.

BATS
Freeman, Don - *Hattie The Backstage Bat*; Viking Penguin Inc., ©1970.
Hoban, Russel - *Lavina Bat*; Holt Assocs., Boston, ©1984.
Kaufmann, John - *Bats in The Dark*; Thomas Y. Crowell Company, NY, ©1972.

BEES
Berenstain, Stan & Jan - *The Big Honey Hunt*; Random House, NY, ©1962.
Petty, Kate - *Bees & Wasps*; Gloucester Press, NY, ©1987.
Pizer, Abigail - *Nosey Gilbert*; Dial Books For Young Readers, NY, ©1987.
Rosen Ellsworth - *To Be A Bee*; Houghton Mifflin Company, Boston, ©1969.

BIRDS
Allred, Mary - *Grandmother Poppy And The Funny-Looking Bird*; Broalman, ©1981.
Bright, Robert - *Georgie And The Baby Birds*; Doubleday Press, NY, ©1983.
Darby, Gene - *What Is A Bird?*; Benefic Press, NY, ©1959.

BLUEJAY
Angelo, Valenti - *The Acorn Tree*; Viking Penguin, Inc. NY, ©P1958.
Freschet, Berniece - *Owl In The Garden*; Lothrop, Lee & Shepard Books, NY, ©1985.
Margolis, Richard J. - *Big Bear, Spare That Tree*; Greenwillow Books, NY, ©1980.

BUGS
Armour, Richard - *Insect All Around Us*; McGraw - Hill Book Company, NY, ©1981.
Danks, Hugh (Dr.) - *The Bug Book*; Workman Publishing, NY ©1987. (comes with book and container for
    bugs)
Gackenbach, Dick - *Little Bug*; Houghton Mifflin/Clarion Books, ©1981.

BUTTERFLY
Gomi, Raro - *Hi, Butterfly!*; William Morrow & Company, NY, ©1983.
Morris, Dean - *Butterflies & Moths*; Raintree Publishers, Milwaukee, WI, ©1988.
Sundgaard, Arnold - *The Lamb & The Butterfly*; Orchard Books, ©1988.

CAMEL
Goodenow, Earle - *The Last Camel*; Walck, ©1968.
Peet, Bill - *Pamela Camel*; Houghton Mifflin, Boston, ©1984.

CATTERPILLAR
Carle, Eric - *The Very Hungry Caterpillar*; Philomel Book, NY, ©1983.
Cornelius, Carol - *Isabella Woolly Bear Tiger Moth*; The Child's World, Elgin, IL, ©1978.
Selsan, Millicent E. & Hunt, Joyce - *A First Look At Caterpillars*; Thomas Allen & Son, ©1987.

CATS/KITTENS
Kanao, Keiko - *Kitten Up A Tree*; Alfred A. Knopf, NY, ©1987.
Szekeres, Cyndy - *Suppertime For Freida Fuzzypaws*; Golden Books, Racine, WI, ©1985.
Thatcher, Hurd - *Axle, The Freeway Cat*; Harper & Row, NY, ©1981.

CENTIPEDE
Free, John Brand - *Life Under A Stone*; B. & C. Black, London, ©1981.

COYOTE
Baylor, Byrd - *Moon Song*; Charles Scribner's Sons, NY, ©1982.
Dolch, Edward W. - *Once There Was A Coyote*; Garrard Publishing Company, Champaign, IL, ©1985.
Nunes, Susan, *Coyote Dreams*; Atheneum, NY, ©1988.

CRICKET
Howe, James - *I Wish I Were A Butterfly*; Harcourt Brace Javanovich, San Diego, CA, ©1985.
Smith, Garry & Vesta - *Clickety Cricket*; Steck - Vaughn Company, Austin, TX, ©1969.

CROCODILE
Croser, Josephine - *Crunch The Crocodile*; Ashton Scholastic, Sydney, Australia, ©1986.
Smith, Mary - *Crocodiles Have Big Teeth All Day*; Follet Publishing Company, Chicago, IL, ©1970.
West, Colin - *Have You Seen A Crocodile?*; J. B. Lippincott, NY, ©1986.

CROW
Hoban, Lillian - *No, No, Sammy Crow*; Greenwillow Books, NY, ©1981.
Holder, Heidi - *Crows*; Farrar, Straus, Giroux, NY, ©1987.
Lionni, Leo - *Six Crows*; Alfred A Knopf; NY, ©1988.

DADDY LONGLEGS/ANANSI
Climo, Shirley - *Someone Saw A Spider*; Thomas Y. Crowell, NY, ©1985.
Hawes, Judy - *My Daddy Longlegs*; Thomas Y. Crowell, NY, ©1972.
Kimmel, Eric A. - *Anasi & The Moss Covered Rock*; Holiday House, NY, ©1988.

DOGS
Lexau, Joan M. - *Come, Sit, Stay*; Franklin Watts, NY, ©1984.
MeRae, Rodney - *The Trouble With Heathrow*; Childrens Press, ©1987.
Thayer, Jane & McCue, Lisa - *The Puppy Who Wanted A Boy*; Mulberry Books, NY, ©1958.

DOODLEBUGS/BEETLES
Johnson, Sylvia A. - *Beetles*; Lerner Publishing Company, Minneapolis, MN, ©1982.

DRAGONFLIES
O'Conner, Jane - *Sir Samll & The Dragonfly*; Random House, NY, ©1988.
Overbeck, Cynthia - *Dragonflies*; Lerner Publishing Company, MA, ©1982.
Suzuki, Yasuo - *Dragonflies*; Wayland Publishing Limited, England, ©1979.

DUCK
Conover, Chris - *Six Little Ducks*; Thomas Y. Crowell, NY, ©1976. (song included in book)
Flack, Marjorie & Wiese, Kurt - *The Story of Ping*; Penguine Books, NY, ©1858.
McCloskey, Robert - *Make Way For Ducklings*; Viking Press, NY, ©1941.

ELEPHANT
Caple, Kathy - *The Biggest Nose*; Houghton Mifflin, Boston, ©1985.
Chorao, Kay - *George Told Kate*; E. P. Dutton, NY, ©1987.
Jenkin-Pearce, Susie - *Bad Boris And The New Kitten*; MacMillian Publishing Company, NY, ©1987.
Posell, Elsa - *Elephants*; Children's Press, Chicago, IL, ©1982.

FAWN/DEER
Arnosky, Jim - *Deer At The Brook*; Lothrop, Lee & Shepard Books, NY, ©1986.
Carrick, Donald - *Harold & The Great Stag*; Clarion Books, NY, ©1988.
Disney, Walt - *Bambi*; Walt Disney Productions, ©1977. (book with cassette)

FIREFLIES
Bolliger, Max - *The Fireflies*; Atheneum, NY, ©1970.
Brinckloe, Julie - *Fireflies*; MacMillan Publishing Company, NY, ©1985.
Eastman, P. D. - *Sam & The Firefly*; Beginner Books, NY, ©1958.
Harris, Louise Dyer - *Flash, The Life Of A Firefly*; Little, NY, ©1966.

GIRAFFE
Cooke, Ann - *Giraffes At Home*; Harper & Row Inc., NY, ©1972.
Hamsa, Bobbie - *Your Pet Giraffe*; Children's Press, Chicago, IL, ©1982.
Sharmat, Marjorie Weinman - *Helga High-Up*; Scholastic Inc., ©1987.

GRASSHOPPERS
Aldridge, Alan - *The Butterfly Ball And The Grasshopper's Feast*; Grossman Publishing, NY, ©1985.
Carey, Bonnie - *Grasshopper To The Rescue*; William Morrow & Company, NY, ©1979.
Lobel, Arnold - *Grasshopper On The Road*; Harper & Row, NY, ©1978.

GROUNDHOG
Bond, Felicia - *Wake Up, Vladimir*; Thomas Y. Crowell, NY, ©1987.
Glass, Marvin - *What Happened Today, Freddy Groundhog*; Crown Publishing Inc., ©1989.

HAMSTER
Blegvad, Lenore - *The Great Hamster Hunt*; Harcourt Brace Jovanovich, Inc., San Diego, CA, ©1969.
Harris, Dorothy Joan - *The School Mouse And The Hamster*; Fredrick Warne & Company, NY, ©1979.
Wolcott, Patty - *Where Did Mat Naughty Little Hamster Go?*; Addison Wesley, ©1984.

HELICOPTER BIRD/HUMMINGBIRD
Gans, Roma - *Hummingbirds In The Garden*; Thomas Y. Crowell, NY, ©1969.

HIPPOPOTAMUS
Moncure, Jane Belk & Gohman, Vera K. - *Yes, No, Little Hippo*; Children's Press, Chicago, IL, ©1988.
Waber, Bernard - *You Look Ridiculous*; Houghton Mifflin, Boston, ©1982.
Ziefer, Harriet & Smith, Mavis - *Harry Takes A Bath*; Viking Kestrel, NY, ©1987.

HORNET
Hutchins, Ross E. - *Paper Hornets*; Addison Wesley Publishing Company, Inc., ©1973.

KANGAROO
Harper, Anita - *Just A Minute*; G. P. Putnam's Sons, NY, ©1987.
Kent, Jack - *Joey*; Prentice-Hall, Inc., ©1984.
Payne, Emmy - *Katy No-Pocket*; Houghton Mifflin, Boston, ©1944.

KOALA
Eberle, Irmengarde - *Koalas Live Here*; Doubleday & Company, Inc., NY, ©1967.
Ruck-Pauguet, Gina - *Oh, That Koala!*; McGraw-Hill, NY, ©1976.
Servent, Vincent - *Koala*; Raintree Children's Books, Milwaukee, WI, ©1985.

LADYBUG
Carle, Eric - *The Grouchy Ladybug*; Thomas Y. Crowell, NY, ©1977.
Pouyanne, Theresa - *The Ladybug*; Rourke Enterprises, Inc. Windermere, FL, ©1988.
Watts, Barrie - *Ladybug*; Silver Burdett Press, Morristown, NJ, ©1987.

MOSQUITO
Aardema, Verna - *Why Mosquitos Buzz In People's Ears*; Dial Books For Young Readers, NY, ©1975.
Mosquito, G. P. Putnam's Sons, NY, ©1982 by Oxford Scientific Films

MUSKRAT
Burgess, Thornton W. - *Jerry Muskrat At Home*; Buccaneer Books, Cutchogue, NY, ©1986.
Dingwall, Laima - *Muskrats*; Grolier Limited, ©1986.
Hoban, Russell - *Harvey's Hideout*; Harper & Row, NY, ©1961.

OWL
Hutchins, Pat - *Good Night, Owl!*; MacMillan Publishing Company, NY, ©1972.
Kalman, Bobbie & Loates, Glen - *Owls*; Crabtree Publishing Company, NY, ©1987.
Stidworth, John & Harris, Alan - *A Year In The Life Of An Owl*; Silver Burdett, Morristown, NJ, ©1987.

PARAKEET
Gordon, Sharon - *Pete The Parakeet*; Troll Assocs., Mahwah, NJ, ©1980.
Graham, Margaret Bloy - *Benjy And The Barking Bird*; Harper & Row Publishing, NY, ©1971.
Sugita, Yutaka - *Casper And The Rainbow Bird*; Barrons/Woodbury, NY ©1978.

PENGUINS
Lepthien, Emilie - *Penquines*; Children's Press, Chicago, IL, ©1983.
Lester, Helen - *Tacky The Penquine*; Houghton Mifflin Company, Boston, ©1988.

PETS
De Hamel, Joan - *Hemi's Pet*; Houghton Mifflin Company, Boston, ©1985.
Chalmers, *Mary - Six Dogs, Twenty-Three Cats, Forty-Five Mice And One Hundred Sixteen Spiders*;
    Harper & Row, NY, ©1986.
Gelman, Rita Golden - *Pets For Sale*; Scholastic Inc., NY, ©1985.

PLATYPUS
Sonnely, Elfie - *A Package For Miss Marshwater*; Dial Books For Young Readers, NY, ©1987.
Stevenson, Susie - *I Forgot*; Orchard Books, NY, ©1988.
Trezise, Percy J. - *Black Duck And Water Rat*; Gareth Stevens Publishing, Milwaukee, WI, ©1988.

PORCUPINE
Dalmais, Anne Marie - *The Porcupine*; Rourke Enterprises, Inc., Winermere, FL, ©1983.
Harshman, Terry Webb - *Porcupine's Pajama Party*; Harper & Row, NY, ©1988.

PRAIRIE
Alibert - Kouraguine, Daniel - *Prairie Dwellers*; Silver Burdett, Morristown, NJ, ©1982.

RABBIT
Billam, Rosemary - *Fuzzy Rabbit In The Park*; Random House, NY, ©1985.
Kraus, Robert - *The Littlest Rabbit*; Harper & Row, NY.
Potter, Beatrix - *The Tale Of Benjamin Bunny*; Fredrick Warne & Company, NY (book with cassette)
Potter, Beatrix - *The Tale Of Peter Rabbit*; Scholastic Inc, NY, ©1986.

RACCOON
Brown, Margaret Wise - *Wait Till The Moon Is Full*; Harper & Row, Pub., NY, ©1948.
Duvoisin, Roger - *Petunia, I Love You*; Alfred A. Knofp, NY, ©1965.
Spanjian, Beth - *Baby Raccoon*; Angel Entertainment Inc., ©1988.

RHINOCEROS
Memling, Carl - *Rupert The Rhinoceros*; Western Publishing Company, NY, ©1960.
Sis, Peter - *Rainbow Rhino*; Alfred A. Knopf, NY, ©1987.
Standon, Anna - *The Singing Rhinoceros*; Coward-McCann, Inc., NY, ©1963.

ROBIN
Kent, Jack - *Round Robin*; Prentice Hall Inc. Englewood Cliffs, NJ, ©1982.
Preston, Edna Mitchell - *Inckle Bickle Robin*; Franklin Wats, NY, ©1973.
Rockwell, Anne - *My Spring Robin*; MacMillan Publishing Company, NY ©1989.

SKUNK
Jones, Chuck - *William The Backwards Skunk*; Crown Publishing Inc., NY, ©1986.
Kitt, Tamera - *A Special Birthday Party For Someone Very Special*; W. W. Norton & Company, Inc., NY, ©1966.
Schlein, Miriam - *What's Wrong With Being A Skunk?*; Four Winds Press, NY, ©1974.
Tether, Graham - *Skunk And Possum*; Houghton Mifflin Company, Boston, MA, ©1979.

SNAKE
Appleby, Leonard - *Snakes*; A & C Black, ©1983.

SQUIRREL
Cosgrove, Stephen - *Crickle-Crack*; Rouke Enterprises, Inc., Vero Beach, FL, ©1987.
Potter, Beatrix - *The Tale Of Squirrel Nitkin*; Talking Caedom, NY, ©1985. (book with cassette)
Young, Miriam - *Miss Suzy*; Parent's Magazine Press, ©1984.

STREAM
Oakley, Graham - *The Church Mice Adrift*; Atheneum, NY, ©1976.

TIGER
Calmenson, Stephanie - *Tiger's Bedtime*; Western Publishing Company, ©1987.
Doods, Siobhan - *Charles Tiger*; Little, Brown & Company, Boston, ©1987.
Roy, Ron - *Old Tiger, New Tiger*; Abigdon, Nashville, TN, ©1978.

TOADS
Gackenbach, Dick - *Crackle Gluck & The Sleeping Toad*; Seabury Press, NY, ©1979.
Lobel, Arnold - *Frog & Toad Together*; Scholastic Inc., NY, ©1972. (series)
Pelty, Kate - *Frogs & Toads*; Franklin Watts, NY, ©1988.

WOODPECKER
Gree, Alain - *Wally The Woodpecker*; Derrydale Brooks, NY, ©1987.
Wildsmith, Brian - *The Owl & The Woodpecker*; Franklin Watts, NY, ©1971.

WOODS/FOREST
Hirschi, Ron - *Who Lives In The Forest?*; Dodd, Mead, & Company, NY, ©1987.

ZEBRA
Goodall, Daphne Machin - *Zebras*; Raintree Publishing Inc., Milwaukee, WI, ©1978.
Hadithi, Mwenye - *Greddy Zebra*; Little Brown & Company, Boston, MA, ©1984.

ZOO
Dolch, Edward W. - *Zoo Is Home*; Garrard Publishing Company, Chapaign, IL, ©1958.
Gibbons, Gail - *Zoo*; Thomas Y. Crowell, NY, ©1987.
Hoban, Tana - *A Children's Zoo*; Greenwillow Books, NY, ©1985.
Jacobsen, Karen - *Zoos*; Children's Press, Chicago, IL, ©1982.

MUSIC & SONGS (RECORDS & CASSETTES)
Birgess, Thornton W. - *Old Mother West Wind*; Spoken Arts, ©1987 (2 cassettes)
Double Dutch Bus & Other Jump Rope Favorites; Wonderland Records, Mountainside, NJ, ©1981
   (record)
Glazer, Tom - *Music For Ones & Twos*; Doubleday Inc., Garden City, NY, ©1984 (song book)

REFERENCE BOOKS FOR TEACHERS
The Animal Kingdom; Greyston Press, NY, ©1954.
National Audubon Society - The Audubon National Encyclopedia; Curtis Publishing Company,
   Philadelphia, PA, ©1965.
Campbell, Bruce - *The Dictionary Of Birds In Color*; Viking Press, NY, ©1974.
Encyclopedia Of The Animal World; Bay Books, Sydney Australia, ©1980.
The Encyclopedia Of Insects; Facts On File Publihers, NY, ©1986.
Grzimek's Animal Life Encyclopedia; Van Nostrand Reinhold Company, NY, ©1975.
The Illustrated Encyclopedia Of The Animal Kingdom; Danbury Press, ©1971.
Line, Les - *The Audubon Society Book of Insects*; Harry N. Abrams, Inc. Publishing, NY, ©1989.
The Marshall Cavendish International Wildlife Encyclopedia; Marshall Cavendish, NY, ©1989.
Parker, Steve - *Mammels*; Alfred A. Knopf Inc., (eye witness book series)
World Book Encyclopedia; World Book Inc., Chicago, IL, ©1989.
Winker, Josef R. (Dr.) - *A Book Of Beetles*; Spring Book, ©1964.

Teachers Notes . . .

Teachers Notes . . .

Teachers Notes . . .

Teachers Notes ...

Teachers Notes . . .

Teachers Notes . . .